Pictured Key
Nature Series

Title:

How To Know

THE WEEDS

Pictured-Keys for identifying the more common weeds of farm and garden, with interesting facts concerning them.

H. E. JAQUES

Professor Emeritus of Biology
Iowa Wesleyan College

WM. C. BROWN COMPANY PUBLISHERS
Dubuque, Iowa

ISBN 0–697–04844–4 (Paper)
ISBN 0–697–04845–4 (Cloth)

Library of Congress Catalog Card Number: 60-2909

THE PICTURED-KEY NATURE SERIES

How To Know The—

AQUATIC PLANTS, Prescott, 1969
BEETLES, Jaques, 1951
BUTTERFLIES, Ehrlich, 1961
CACTI, Dawson, 1963
EASTERN LAND SNAILS, Burch, 1962
ECONOMIC PLANTS, Jaques, 1948, 1958
FALL FLOWERS, Cuthbert, 1948
FRESHWATER ALGAE, Prescott, 1954, 1970
FRESHWATER FISHES, Eddy, 1957, 1969
GRASSES, Pohl, 1953, 1968
GRASSHOPPERS, Helfer, 1963
IMMATURE INSECTS, Chu, 1949
INSECTS, Jaques, 1947
LAND BIRDS, Jaques, 1947
LICHENS, Hale, 1969
LIVING THINGS, Jaques, 1946
MAMMALS, Booth, 1949, 1970
MARINE ISOPOD CRUSTACEANS, Schultz, 1969
MOSSES AND LIVERWORTS, Conard, 1944, 1956
PLANT FAMILIES, Jaques, 1948
POLLEN AND SPORES, Kapp, 1969
PROTOZOA, Jahn, 1949
ROCKS AND MINERALS, Helfer, 1970
SEAWEEDS, Dawson, 1956
SPIDERS, Kaston, 1952
SPRING FLOWERS, Cuthbert, 1943, 1949
TAPEWORMS, Schmidt, 1970
TREMATODES, Schell, 1970
TREES, Jaques, 1946
WATER BIRDS, Jaques-Ollivier, 1960
WEEDS, Jaques, 1959
WESTERN TREES, Baerg, 1955

FOREWORD

HE word "WEED" may have many definitions such as an unwanted plant; an unsightly, useless or harmful plant; any plant growing in cultivated ground to the injury of the crop or desired vegetation; plant growth that gives an unfavorable appearance to an area, etc. Thus it will be seen that it is not the species that brands a plant a weed, but its associates and how it lives. Many highly useful species may become objectionable weeds when in the wrong place. One frequently sees scattered stalks of corn growing in an otherwise beautiful field of soybeans. Such plants are a hindrance and, thus situated, are as definitely weeds as plants of the common milkweed or velvetleaf would be.

The Pictured-Key books are designed primarily to be identification manuals. The purpose of this book is to make easy the determination of many of the weeds one is likely to find among growing plants. In the school room it is a matter of education and of training for future use; anywhere a careful study of weeds may become an interesting pastime. Weeds are never lacking in abundance and no one objects to their being collected.

When working in the garden or cutting a patch of weeds we have found that naming the species of plants as they fall before the hoe or scythe makes an excellent dispeller of monotony. One may become so interested that he even regrets when the otherwise boring task is completed.

This book has been in preparation for a considerable period of years. Many of our college students have worked at the drawings or made seed counts and other research data now used in the book. We would like to mention all of them but the list is too long for that.

Large numbers of drawings were made by Francesca Jaques Stoner and by Marshall Thayer.

We are truly grateful for the splendid reception that has been accorded the Pictured-Key books and hope this volume may likewise prove helpful in many ways.

Mt. Pleasant, Iowa
August 1, 1959

CONTENTS

SOME FACTS ABOUT WEEDS

 **T**HE purpose of this book is to make possible the easy identification of our common weeds. Almost every one is familiar with many of the basic botanical facts which need to be understood in studying plants. We are, however, briefly reviewing some of the essential items used in describing plants so that they will be handy for reference.

All living things are either plants or animals. Ever since Aristotle's day (384-322 B. C.) scientists have been making lists of known plants and animals with the result that at the present time some 400,000 known species of plants have been named and described (are "known to science"). Large as this number appears it is greatly outtopped by the animals, for well over a million species of animal life are known.

Almost all of our common weeds belong to the flowering or seed-bearing group of plants which numbers about a quarter million species. Our list is fairly complete for the common weeds of our region, yet we have dealt with less than 400 species. It will be thus noted that a relatively small percentage of plants falls in the category of weeds.

NAMES

Each plant has a technical name which was given it by the scientist who first described it. It often also has one or more common names. The scientific name consists of two parts, the genus name (which begins with a capital letter) and which is followed by the species name (beginning with a small letter). Since scientific names are the same in all languages, they should be used when one wishes to be assured of accuracy. A species is sometimes divided into *subspecies* or *varieties*. These are designated by a word following the species name to form a *trinomial*. Common names (often called English names) are frequently numerous for the same plant and still worse, the same common name may be applied to several different plants by different people, which becomes very confusing. Weeds are so well known that many of them have accumulated numerous common names. It will be noted that we give several common names for many of the weeds we describe. To select one common name for each weed and thus attempt to standardize weed literature would seem to be a hopeless undertaking.

1

HOW TO KNOW THE WEEDS

PLANT PARTS

Roots, stems, leaves, flowers, fruit, and seeds are the important parts of a plant. Fig. 1.

Roots may be fibrous or fleshy. They absorb nutriments, anchor the plants, form new plants, and serve for storage.

Stems support the leaves and reproductive parts of the plant, transport raw and organized food materials, become storage organs, and develop new plants.

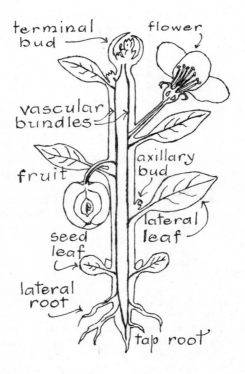

Figure 1

Leaves, usually green, do most of the work of food manufacture (photosynthesis). They often serve, too, as storage organs. Their shape and arrangement offer excellent characters for plant identification. Fig. 2.

2

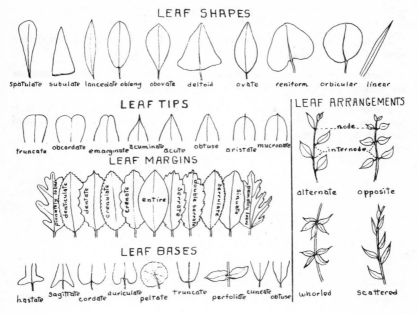

Figure 2

Flowers are for sexual reproduction and make possible the formation of fruit and seeds. Classification of plants is based more largely on flower structure than any other one feature.

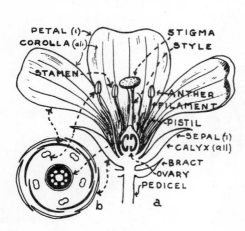

Figure 3

Complete flowers have all four parts (Fig. 3); *sepals, petals, stamens,* and *pistil.* In many flowers (*incomplete*) one or more of these parts are absent. Sepals are the outer leaf-like parts of a bud; collectively they make the *calyx.* They may be distinct or more or less united with each other at their edges. Above and inside the calyx is the *corolla.* Its individual parts are petals. Petals may be distinct or united to each other thus often forming tubular flowers as in the

3

morning-glory. The next whorl of floral parts carries the stamens. A stamen consists of an *anther* which is supported on an often-thread-like *filament*. The normal anther has two chambers which bear pollen grains. Centermost at the tip of the flowering stem (*pedicel*) stands the

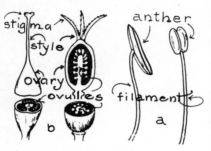

pistil consisting of an *ovary*, *style*, and *stigma*. One to many ovules are borne in the ovary. Fig. 4. Each ovule is a potential seed but in order to develop it must be fertilized by the union of a male sperm with the female egg within the ovule. This is preceded by *pollination;* the transfer of pollen grains from the anther to

Figure 4

the stigma, F. When a pollen grain reaches a stigma, it grows a pollen tube the tip of which presently reaches the ovule. By that time the egg cell has been formed in the ovule and two sperm cells formed within the tip of the pollen tube. One of these sperm cells fuses with the egg cell. Fig. 5. This fertilized egg soon becomes a seed which is just an embryonic plant with sufficient food materials to permit it to become independent when germination takes place.

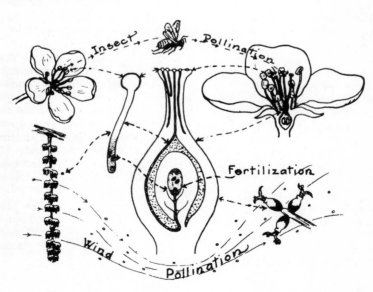

Figure 5

4

In order for a seed to germinate, it must have moisture and a favorable temperature. Some seeds retain their viability for only a short period and will die if growth is not permitted. On the other hand there are seeds which require a rest period (dormancy) before they will germinate at all. The seeds of most cultivated crops will safely pass one or two winters and germinate favorably but the viability of many species drops off rather sharply after the second or third year. Such seeds are soon found to be lifeless.

The seeds of many species of weeds are much longer lived, some germinating after a rest of fifty years or more. After moisture and temperature have been applied and germination is well started, there seems to be no way to reverse the process and return the seeds to their dormant conditions.

It is very interesting to note the high prolificacy of many plants. Nature seems to have the rate of reproduction of her creatures adjusted to the normal hazards of a species. Many weeds are exceptionally prolific. An average corn plant will produce from 600-2000 kernels of corn thus having the ability to multiply itself 2000 fold. To bring in some mature weed plants and by counting and estimating the seeds actually produced and thus get figures on their productivity makes an interesting school project. Some rather amazing figures are thus found.

A plant of the Common Cattail was found to produce more than a million seeds in its one spike while weed species maturing well over 50,000 viable seeds are not uncommon. Since any one of these seeds under favorable conditions could replace the parent plant, it is little wonder that man's fight with weeds may sometimes seem to be a losing one.

One fall semester a laboratory section in General Botany thus computed the seeds of 25 species of common weeds, all taken from gardens near the college. Except for the Common Cattail, Lamb's Quarters proved to be the most prolific species studied. One quite large plant (plants of average size were usually selected) bore the amazing number of 934,911 seeds. Fifteen other medium sized specimens of this same species averaged 27,940 seeds per plant. The least prolific of the 25 species was a wild rose which counted out only 175 seeds for one specimen and 793 as an average for the 25 specimens examined. One Golden Rod plant produced 146,250 seeds with an average of 47,024 for the seven plants studied.

Six species of grasses were studied. Witch Grass was the high one with one plant having 56,400 seeds. The average for its 10 specimens was 19,730. Ten plants of Green Amaranth averaged 27,537 seeds while fourteen plants of the rather modest Wild Peppergrass yielded an average of 24,241 seeds per plant.

AGE

Some plants live a normal life of less than one year. They germinate from the seed, attain full size, produce flowers, fruit, and seeds, then dry up and die regardless of the weather or growing conditions. Such plants are said to be *annuals*. In temperate regions annuals start each spring as seedlings. Some plants germinate from seeds in the late summer or fall and store nourishment to carry through the winter. With the coming of spring they soon flower, mature seeds and die, all in less than 12 months. Such plants are *winter annuals* and may be noxious weeds as their seeds are mature before the farmer is thinking to cut weeds to prevent seeding.

At the other extreme are long-lived plants which go on growing and maturing seeds year after year somewhat indefinitely. These *perennials* are usually woody, especially in temperate regions, although some species of plants have perennial roots which grow new herbaceous tops each year. The percentage of annual weeds and of perennial weeds is about equal.

A much smaller number of weeds, percentage wise, are *biennials*, which as the words seem to indicate live two years. Their usual plan is to grow vegetatively the first year, and store a large amount of food reserves in enlarged roots, leaves, or stems. Then the second growing season is given to the production of flowers, fruit, and seeds. When the seed crop is matured, the store of nutriment is exhausted and the plant dies. An interesting variation of this pattern is seen in the Century Plant which stuffs its thickened leaves with plant foods for 15 to 20 years, then grows a tall flowering stem. After a few months flowers change to fruit with seeds, while the many once-thick leaves wither, droop, and die, leaving only a wreck of the former noble plant.

VEGETATIVE REPRODUCTION

New plants that grow from seeds have two parents and represent sexual reproduction. That is Nature's scheme of increasing varieties and making vigorous offsprings. Many plants may, also, multiply themselves by vegetative methods. The new plants thus formed have the same inheritance as the one parent and under usual conditions will be very much like it. Roots and special root structures, stems and leaves may in some plants develop new individuals.

Bulbs, corms, bulbils, rhizomes, etc., are specialized vegetative parts which function in reproducing new plants. Weeds seemingly reproduce both sexually and vegetatively more abundantly than cultivated plants.

WEED DISSEMINATION

Weeds have many ingenious ways of widening their occupied areas. Seeds likely account for the most successful spreading of weeds. Seeds for farm or garden, if carelessly selected, may contain a fairly large percentage of weed seed. Seeds for planting should be closely inspected and if found to contain much weed seed or even a few seeds of any highly objectionable species, be cleaned or rejected. Some serious weed pests produce seeds so closely resembling in size and weight those of a cultivated crop that their separation from the crop seeds is very difficult.

HOW TO KNOW THE WEEDS

Numerous species of weed produce seeds bearing tufts of hair or thin membraneous wings to permit the seeds to be carried long distances by the wind. A few species of weeds break near the ground and shake out their seeds as the wind rolls the plant from place to place. Water likewise carries seeds of many species and deposits them on overflowed fields or other spots favorable for their growth.

Seeds which adhere by barbed or hooked spines to clothing of man or to the hairy coats of animals are in that way widely scattered. Birds and other animals carry and scatter undigested seeds which have been eaten and pass unharmed through the digestive tract.

Packing materials often contain many weed seeds. Seeds scatter from trucks and railroad cars as they pass along the highways. Every botanist knows that railroad right of ways are ideal collecting grounds where plants new to the region are frequently found.

Farm machinery when moved from one field to another often carries weeds to a new location.

Birds and stray animals may carry weed seed in mud on their feet.

Some very serious weeds have been imported and grown as ornamentals to presently escape and become pests.

Some weeds if cut in the early flowering stage possess the ability to mature their seeds. Such plants need to be burned.

WEED ORIGINS

It will be noted that a large percentage of our weeds are not native plants. They have come to us from other countries where they have had centuries of experience in thriving in spite of the efforts of farmers and gardeners to eradicate them. Europe has supplied a large percentage of our most common weeds.

WEEDS ARE COSTLY

The loss due to weeds in farms and gardens takes several forms and is often heavier than recognized. The presence of weeds in hay or of weed parts in threshed grain reduces the value and grade of these feeds.

Many weeds in growing require more water and plant minerals than the cultivated plants with which they are associated. They may also seriously compete for light. Insect pests and plant diseases may start on weeds and later transfer to the crop plant. Weeds are costly; it does not pay to tolerate them.

Prevention makes the best start in weed control. Good farm practices from year to year leave the soil with relatively few weed seeds. Then if the farmer sees to it that he plants only clean seeds there will be fewer weeds with which to contend. As far as possible weeds should not be permitted to mature seeds. Good cultivation should aim at getting all the weeds when they are small and while they are doing but mimum damage.

7

HOW TO KNOW THE WEEDS

Some weeds such as Canadian Thistle, Quackgrass, etc., multiply so rapidly by a spreading root system that they completely take over patches of ground to the exclusion or choking out of practically all other plants. Sodium chlorate or any of several other chemicals will permanently kill such patches but will leave the plot of ground sterile to the growth of any plants from one to several years, depending upon the chemical used and the strength with which it is applied.

Selective chemicals have come into popular use in recent years. They derive their name and value through their ability to kill certain species of plants while others are left unharmed. Most common are those that kill *broadleaf* plants but which are tolerated by many monocotyledons. Such *herbicides* are usefully employed to destroy broadleaf weeds in fields or small grain or to spray roadsides to make possible pure stands of grasses. They are sometimes also used in roadside spraying where volunteer trees and shrubs are abundant. Such jobs are sometimes so poorly done that the roadside is left much more unsightly with dead brush and partly killed trees than it was in the first place.

GENERAL PRINCIPLES FOR WEED CONTROL

The following seven general principles are quoted from Farm Weed of Canada.

1. There is no weed known which cannot be eradicated by constant attention, if the nature of its growth be understood.

2. Never allow weeds to ripen seeds.

3. Cultivate frequently, particularly early in the season so as to destroy seedlings.

4. Many weed seeds can be induced to germinate in autumn by cultivating stubbles immediately after harvest. Most of these seedlings will be winter killed or can be easily disposed of by plowing or cultivation in spring.

5. All weeds bearing mature seeds should be burnt. Under no circumstances should they be plowed under.

6. All weeds can be destroyed by use of ordinary implements of the farm, the plow, the cultivator, the harrow, the spud and the hoe.

7. Be constantly on the alert to prevent new weeds from becoming established.

THE HELPFUL SIDE

Weeds are sometimes thought of as a punishment for man. They actually do many helpful things. Cultivating to uproot and destroy the weeds loosens the soil, thus making possible for air and water to more easily reach the roots of the crop plants. Under some conditions weeds, when permitted to grow alongside of cultivated plants, so shade these plants from hot, drying sun that plants thus protected yield more abundantly than others which are exposed to the sun's rays.

HOW TO KNOW THE WEEDS

Weeds when plowed under enrich the soil by adding humus and minerals. It should be noted, however, that the minerals thus returned to the soil are only those that the weeds have previously taken from the soil, except in the case of leguminous weeds.

THE HERBARIUM

An excellent means of familiarizing one-self with the names of weeds is to make a herbarium or collection of pressed specimens. Representative pieces of the plants are collected and pressed for drying between folded newspapers. When well pressed and dried, they are mounted on heavy paper and labeled. Looseleaf scrapbooks (about 10" x 12" or larger) are excellent for this. See "How to Know the Spring Flowers" page 15 or "How to Know the Fall Flowers" page 12 for detailed instruction for making a herbarium.

Such a collection is excellent for reference, but likely its greatest value and source of satisfaction is in the work of making it.

HOW TO USE THE KEYS

Keys offer one of the easiest and most accurate ways of finding the correct name for a plant. It will be noted that the key statements are set in pairs of opposing characters. The statements of the pair are numbered alike but lettered differently to distinguish them. Whenever a drawing would make the meaning clearer a "picture" has been added to the statement. This is one of the helpful characteristics of the Pictured-Key books.

Neigbor Brown comes over with a new weed he has "been seeing in his garden." Can we tell him its name? So we have a chance to try out our new weed book. Comparing Brown's specimen with 1a and 1b, it is easily seen that 1a applies since both flowers and seeds are in evidence. The figure at the right of the page directs us to 5a, 5b where we see that the net veined leaves make our plant a Dicotyledon and sends us to page 44.

Then with both calyx and corolla present we find 1b under *DICOTYLEDONS* directing us to 39 where we note that the petals are separate from each other (39a) and under 40a that the ovary is superior (up within the flower) thus directing us to 41. Since the carpels are more than 1 we are guided to 64. The stamens being more than 10 we go on to find that 65b fits our plant; 66b directs us to 69 since the leaves are "not dotted" and since the stamens are united in a central column. We find our plant must belong to the Mallow Family. The fruit is plainly a 5-celled capsule with several seeds in each cell (carpel) which information leads us from 71a to 72a. Now we compare our specimen with the description. The hairy, lobed leaves and the rather large pale yellow flowers with deep purple eye, etc., plainly mark the plant so we can tell Mr. Brown quite positively that his weed is the Flower-of-an-hour and that the scientific name is *Hibiscus trionum* L. (the L. indicates that the name was given by Linnaeus who is called in this case the author or authority).

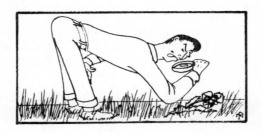

PICTURED-KEYS FOR DETERMINING MANY COMMON WEEDS

1a Plants which produce flowers and seeds........................5

1b Plants reproducing by spores; never having flowers or seeds....2

2a Independently growing green fern plants......................4

2b Parasitic or saprophitic fungi; not green....................3

3a Mushrooms or toadstool-like plants. Fig. 6.........*Aminita* spp.

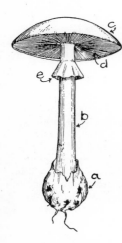

The mushroom pictured here is the "Death Angel," *Aminita phalloides* (Vaill.) a, volva; b, stem; c, cap; d, gills; e, ring. Most of the members of this genus are highly poisonous. The cup (which entirely surrounds the plant when young, making it egg-shaped) is a distinguishing character of the genus. This mushroom is variable in color, usually white, yellowish or dull green but sometimes darker.

Figure 6

It is not our intention to include the fungi among the weeds but we mention these and Ergot, which follows, only because of their poisonous properties.

Hundreds of species of mushrooms occur throughout our region, most of which are edible but a few species are deadly poisonous and annually contribute their share to the list of tragic deaths. The several poisonous species, which frequently grow in close association with the others, are very definitely "weeds" and extremely serious ones for the mushroom grower or collector.

3b Enlarged dark purplish bodies rather frequently seen in the heads of rye and other grasses. Fig. 7...ERGOT, *Claviceps purpurea* Tul.

The "plant" part of this pest makes its filamentous growth within the tissue of its host and is apparent, externally, only in its fruiting. Occasional grains of the grass host are so invaded by the parasite that they attain several times their normal size. These hard purplish bodies are known as *sclerotia*, and are poisonous to man and domestic animals. Rye is likely its most common host. Care needs to be given to assure that it is cleaned from grain before being ground or fed.

Figure 7

Many species of fungi live as parasites within the tissues of other plants. It would require a sizeable book to treat even only the more important ones.

4a Plants with expanded and much cut leaves. Fig. 8.............
.....................BRACKEN FERN, *Pteridium aquilinum* (L.)

Perennial, reproducing by spores and spreading from under-ground rootstocks which may attain a length of several feet; leaves (a) 1-3 ft. long, broadly triangular and divided into 3 parts; spores borne on underside of leaflets (b) within the infolded margins (c). The young leaves arise as "fiddle-head" fronds (d).

Widely distributed in upland thickets and becoming a weed in pastures and recently cleared fields. Hogs eat the root stocks and sheep will keep the plants closely cropped in pastures. There is some evidence that the plant may be poisonous to cattle when consumed in large quantities.

Figure 8

Other common names: Common Brake, Hog Brake, Eagle-fern, Lady-bracken, Upland-fern.

Several other species of ferns may persist for a time when wooded areas are cleared.

4b Plants the chief structure of which are cylindrical hollow stems; much branched in this species. Fig. 9.........................
.......................FIELD HORSETAIL, *Equisetum arvense* L.

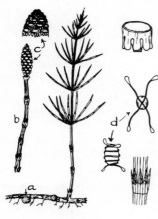

Perennial, producing spores instead of seeds and spreading by underground rootstocks which often bear small tubers (a). The round, hollow stems are much branched and attain various heights up to 2 ft. These vegetative plants are preceded in early spring by fleshy, unbranched, fertile stems (b) 4-10 inches high, yellowish or pinkish and terminating in a spore-bearing cone (c); the tubers and fleshy rhizomes produced the previous summer, of course, supply the food for growing these structures. It is often common in moist places and sometimes quite persistent. (d) spores with elaters.

Figure 9

Other common names: Horsetail Fern, Cornfield Horsetail, Bottle-brush, Snake Grass, Horse Pipes, Pine Grass, Meadow Pine, Devil's Guts, Toad Pipes.

Several other species are less common and not so likely to be weedy. They are usually unbranched and bear the fruiting cone on the green vegetative stem. The stems of all of these species are heavily impregnated with silica and are injurious to horses and cattle if eaten in large quantities.

5a Weeds that are grass-like (a); leaves long and narrow with parallel veins (a); flowering parts, when present, in 3's (b). Fig. 10. MONOCOTYLEDONS.........6

Figure 10

5b Weeds not grass-like, leaves usually net veined (a); flowering parts in 4's or 5's (b). Fig. 11. DICOTYLEDONS..page 44

Figure 11

MONOCOTYLEDONS

6a Carpels one; flowers minute, surrounded by chaffy bracts (glumes); without a 3-parted perianth; flowers grouped in spikes or spikelets; fruit an achene or grain. Fig. 12. GRASSES and SEDGES......9

Figure 12

6b Flowers not in chaffy bracts or scales...........................7

7a Flowers in cylindrical, terminal spikes; tall, coarse plants growing in marshy places. Fig. 13a..COMMON CAT-TAIL, *Typha latifolia* L.

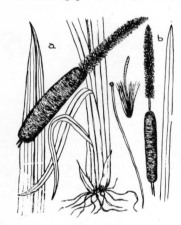

Figure 13

Coarse, sturdy perennial, 4—8 ft. high; growing in marshy places; spreading by creeping rootstocks. It is widely distributed.

Leaves ¼—1 in. wide. The conspicuous terminal spike is 3—12 in. long and often an inch or more in diameter and is dark brown or blackish at maturity and often bears a million or more seeds. The staminate flowers occur immediately above the seed bearing part of the spike.

Other names: Broad leaved Cat-tail, Cat-o-nine-tails, Cooper's Reeds, Reed-mace, Cat-tail Flag, Black-sap, Bullrush, Blackamoor, Candlewick, Water-torch, Flax tail.

NARROWED-LEAVED CAT-TAIL *Typha angustifolia* L. (Fig. 19b), an Eurasian plant is widely scattered and may be recognized by its narrow leaves and head.

7b Not as in 7a..8

8a Slender, grass-like plants, as pictured, growing in marshy places; with 6 narrow similar sepals and petals, and 6 united carpels separating at maturity. Fig. 14..ARROW-GRASS, *Triglochin maritima* L.

This little herb, ½—2 ft. high, is of particular interest because it is poisonous to livestock. The slender leaves are semi-cylindrical and up to 15 inches long. The greenish flowers and fruit are borne in a slender raceme; the fruit is 6-parted. It grows in salt marshes (sometimes in fresh water) and while not especially common, ranges entirely across our continent. It blooms in the summer and fall.

Other names: Spike Grass, Salt-marsh Arrow Grass.

Figure 14

8b Carpels three, united into one compound ovary. Fig. 15 ....55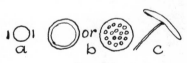

Figure 15

9a Leaves two-ranked (in two rows on the stem) (a), the edges of their sheaths not united; stems cylindrical (or oval) in cross section (b) and almost always hollow; anthers attached to the filament by their middle (c); fruit a grain. Fig. 16. GRASSES.......10

Figure 16

9b Leaves three-ranked (in three rows on the stem) the edges of their sheaths united; stems almost always triangular in cross section and solid; anthers attached at one end; fruit an achene. Fig. 17. SEDGES 52

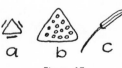

Figure 17

15

GRASS FAMILY

10a Spikelets (1-5) inclosed within a spine-covered, bur-like, spherical involucre. Fig. 18........SANDBUR, *Cenchrus longispinus* **(Hack.)**

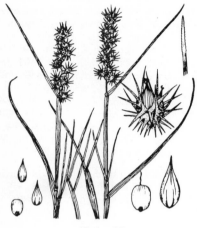

Figure 18

Annual or perennial, low growing, m u c h branched; stems to 1½ ft. or more; flattened sheaths with ciliated margins, otherwise glabrous; leaf-blades about ¼ in. wide. Fruit a dehiscent spiny bur, which becomes readily attached to the hairs of animals and the clothing of man. July —Oct.

What is now considered several species, was named *C. tribuloides* by Linnaeus. Anyone who has attempted to remove some of these burs sees the sense to the Linnean name. *C. longispinus* grows in sandy places widely distributed throughout the U. S., while *C. tribuloides*, a larger, coarser plant, is confined principally to sandy beaches along the Atlantic and Gulf coasts.

Other names: Bear-grass, Sand-spurs, Cock-spurs.

10b Spikelets not in a spiny involucre............................11

11a Flowers 2 or more to each spikelet............................35

11b Flowers only one to each spikelet (or if, as rarely, 2 or 3, then the lower ones sterile)............................12

12a (a, b, c) Spikelets arranged in panicles or spike-like racemes. Fig. 19 17

Figure 19

12b Spikelets arranged in 2 rows along one side of a flattened stem..13

12c Spikelets in a solitary terminal spike, arranged in 2 rows on opposite sides; spikelets 2 or 3 at each node. Fig. 20.
. 16

Figure 20

13a Plants arising from the nodes of long, creeping rootstalks (rhizomes). Fig. 21. . . . . BERMUDA GRASS, *Cynodon dactylon* (L.)

Figure 21

Perennial (sometimes annual), spreading by long, creeping rootstocks, 4—12 in. long. Stem reclining, flattened, wiry; blades 1—2 in. long, narrow; sheaths usually glabrous, with white hairs on the ligule, crowded at the base and along the stolons. The spikes, ½—2 in. long are borne in 4's and 5's on the stem.

It was introduced from Europe and has been used as a pasture plant. Abundant throughout the South especially in sandy places. July—Sept.

Other names: Bahama-grass, Wire-grass, Dog's-tooth-grass, Canegrass, Indian Doob, Scutch-grass.

13b Plants not arising from creeping rootstalks. 14
14a The lower flowering glume (lemma) thick, the margin not translucent but rolled inward; perennials. Fig. 22. . . . .
. . . .(a) PASPALUM, *Paspalum ciliatifolium* Michx.

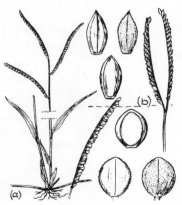

Figure 22.

Much branching perennial, 1—2 ft. high; blades ½ in. wide and up to 10 in. long, glabrous, often with minute hairs on the margins; racemes one to three, only one terminal.

A native plant rather common from Maryland, southward. June—Aug.

Other name: Ciliate-leaved Paspalum.

(b) WIRE-GRASS
Paspalum distichum L.

This native perennial spreads readily by jointed rootstocks and becomes a persistent weed. Height

17

½—2 ft., sheaths smooth, blades 2—5 in. long; racemes 1—2 in. long, usually in pairs but occasionally 3. It is found from Virginia southward and westward to the Pacific Coast. Aug.—Sept.

Other names: Devil's-grass, Joint-grass, Knotgrass, Seaside-millet.

14b The lower flowering glume (lemma) thin with flat, translucent margin; annuals **15**

15a Leaves usually over ¼ inch wide and very hairy; pedicels with sharp angles. Fig. 23..
................**LARGE CRABGRASS,** *Digitaria sanguinalis* **(L.)**

Annual, erect or reclining, frequently taking root at the lower nodes; 1—3 ft. long; blades about 1/3 in. wide and 2—6 in. in length; racemes 3-10 all arising from near the top of the stem, often purplish.

Naturalized from Europe and w i d e l y distributed throughout North America as a very persistent weed. It develops rapidly, crowding out other plants. July—Sept.

Other names: Finger-grass, Purple Crab-grass, Pigeon - g r a s s, Crowfoot, Polish Millet.

Figure 23

15b Leaves not over ¼ inch wide; glabrous; often tinged with purple; pedicels cylindrical, smooth. Fig. 24...........................
...........**SMALL CRABGRASS,** *Digitaria ischaemum* **(Schreb.)**

Annual, culms erect or decumbent, often rooting at the lower nodes; ½—2 ft. long; blades narrow, 1—3 in. long.

Introduced from Europe, it has become widespread in our country. It and the preceding quickly spring up from the seemingly ever-present seeds in thin places in lawns and crowd out other grass plants. It makes a good cover for a short time but soon turns brown, dies and leaves a more unsightly place than before. July—Sept.

Figure 24

Other names: Finger-grass, Smooth Finger-grass.

16a Low-growing rigid plants (usually less than 1 ft. high); empty glumes unlike in width. Fig. 25. . . . .
. . . . LITTLE BARLEY, *Hordeum pusillum* Nutt.

Annual, 5—15 in. high; leaf blades erect, roughened above, smooth below, ½—3 in. long, narrow sheaths usually shorter than internodes, loose-fitting; spike 1—3 in. long, spikelets usually in threes, grain yellow.

It prefers dry soil and is a native of our western states but has spread eastward, especially in the South. May—July.

WILD BARLEY, *H. nodosum* L. is a somewhat similar but larger plant (up to 2 ft.). All of its empty scales are bristle-like, whreeas in *pusillum* some of the empty scales are dilated above the base.

Figure 25

16b Taller, more flexible plants with somewhat drooping heads which bear long (1½—2½ in.) yellowish-green or purplish bristles (awns); winter annual. Fig. 26. . . . .
. . . . SQUIRREL-TAIL GRASS, *Hordeum jubatum* L.

Winter annual, 1—2 ft. high; leaf blades narrow, 1—5 in. long, sheaths shorter than the internode; spike 2—4 in. long with long silky awns and quite conspicuous.

Apparently introduced from Europe and now widely spread along roadsides, and in pastures, meadows and waste places. July—Aug.

Other names: Flicker-tail-grass, W i l d Barley, Skunk - tail - grass, Tickle-grass, Foxtail-grass.

Figure 26

17a One sterile flowering glume in each spikelet, below the fertile flower 18

17b But one fertile flower in each spikelet, with no sterile flower
(glume) 25

18a Lower empty glume smaller than the second; spikelets not covered
with silky hairs, all fertile...................................20

18b Lower empty glume larger than the second; spikelets covered with
silky hairs and containing a sessile fertile flower and one or two
pedicelled, sterile flowers...................................19

19a Spikelets purplish, grouped in threes, one of which is fertile, the
other two sterile or rudimentary; large coarse grass with leaves ½
to 1½ in. wide. Fig. 27..JOHNSON-GRASS, Sorgum halepense (L.)

Figure 27

Perennial, spreading by many rootstocks; rather coarse heavy plant growing to a height of 3—5 ft.; leaves with a width up to 1 inch and a length up to 2 feet. Flowers and fruit in an open panicle often a foot or more in length. Grain reddish-brown, about 1/10 in. long. June—July.

Man learns slowly. Johnson-grass, an European import, was once widely advertised and planted. It does produce quantities of palatable forage but knows nothing about withdrawing from the stage when the scenes change. It was one thing to start it but quite another to kill it out. It is widely scattered especially in our warmer areas and like the English Sparrow will likely be with us forever.

Many names have helped the more to sell it. A few are: Morocco-millet, Mean's-grass, False Guinea-grass, Cuba-grass, St. Mary's-grass, Millet-grass, Egyptian-millet, Evergreen-millet, Maiden-cane.

19b Spikelets grouped in 2's, the sessile one being fertile and the one on a pedicel rudimentary. Fig. 28..........................
.....................BEARD-GRASS, *Andropogon virginicus* L.

An erect perennial, 1½—4 ft. tall; sheaths often hirsute, blades 6—18 in. long and up to ¼ in wide; racemes in 2's (rarely 3's or 4's) with a silky pubescence and 1—2½ in. long. July—Sept.

This native plant is widely scattered but most troublesome in the South.

Other names: Sedge-grass, Broomsedge.

The genus contains a good number of native grasses. Two others that are sometimes considered w e e d s are FORKED BEARD-GRASS, *A. furcatus* Muhl. and BROOM-BEARD-GRASS, *A. scoparis* Michx.

Figure 28

20a Fruiting head finger-like, resembling a slender bottle brush; spikelets surrounded by a bristly involucre. Fig. 29 23

Figure 29

20b Fruiting head an open panicle; spikelets without involucre.....21
21a Panicle symmetrical 22
21b Panicle one-sided; each spikelet with one long bristle. Fig. 30...
...................BARNYARD-GRASS, *Echinochloa crus-galli* (L.)

This coarse-growing, European annual is widely scattered and often very common. Erect or reclining with culms 2—4 ft. long; blades ½ in. or more wide and a foot or more in length. The heavy, coarse panicles are frequently purplish. July—Sept.

Other names: Panic-grass, Water-grass, Cockspur-grass, Cocksfoot.

A variety, *edulis*, has been promoted for forage under the names Japanese-Barnyard-millet and Billion-dollar-grass, Cockspur-grass.

Figure 30

22a Plants thickly covered with long, soft hairs. Fig. 31 . . . .
. . . . **WITCH GRASS,** *Panicum capillare* L.

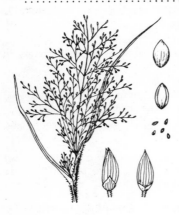

Annual, 1—2 ft. high; sheaths heavily covered with hispid hairs; blade 6—12 in. long and around ½ in. wide, covered with appressed hairs. Panicle often a foot high with very numerous tiny spikelets. When ripened and dry the entire panicle breaks off and rolls along the ground when blown by the wind. This unique scheme of seed distribution has given it the name "Tumble-weed." It ranges throughout our country but seems to be most abundant in the eastern and central parts. July—Sept.

Other names: Tickle-grass, Fool-hay, Old Witch-grass, Tumble Panic-grass.

Figure 31

22b Plants glabrous; a much branched, somewhat decumbent annual. Fig. 32 . . . .
. . . . . **SPROUTING CRAB-GRASS,** *Panicum dichotomiflorum* Michx.

A native annual, 1—2 ft. high; sheaths open, glabrous; blades ½ to 2 ft. long and around ½ in. wide. It roots at the lower nodes and becomes very abundant in gardens, wet fields, along roadsides and in waste places. The sheaths are sometimes purplish. Its characters differ so widely that several varieties have been named. July—Sept.

Other names: Spreading Witchgrass, Spreading Panic-grass.

Figure 32

23a Bristles green or purplish, 1—3 to each spikelet; in fruit, seeds smaller **24**

23b Bristles tawny yellow, 5 or more for each spikelet; leaf blade with long hairs on upper surface near the stem, seeds considerably larger than in 22a. Fig. 33..YELLOW FOXTAIL, *Setaria glauca* (L.)

Figure 33

This very common, usually erect annual attains a height of 1 to 4 ft. The sheaths and blades are glabrous, the latter having a length of 2—6 in. and a width up to 1/3 in. The rather long, brownish-yellow bristles and fairly large seeds distinguish it from the other foxtails. July—Sept.

It abounds in stubble fields, cultivated ground and neglected places. It was introduced from Europe.

Other names: Pigeon-grass, Glaucous bristly foxtail, Wild millet, Summer-grass, Golden foxtail, Bristlegrass.

24a Barbs on the bristles pointed downward, causing the heads to become attached to each other and to passing animals. Fig. 34....
.....................BRISTLY FOXTAIL, *Setaria verticillata* (L.)

Figure 34

An annual 1—2 ft. high, erect or decumbent and somewhat branched. The comparatively wide blades are 2—8 in. long while the heads have a length of 2—3 in. July—Sept.

This European plant becomes an annoying pest in gardens and fields when once established. It is readily recognized by the way it adheres to clothing and the hair of animals.

Other names: Bur foxtail, Brown foxtail, Rough foxtail-grass.

24b Barbs on the bristles pointing upward; leaf blade smooth. Fig. 35.
......................GREEN FOXTAIL, *Setaria viridis* (L.)

A simple or branched annual up to 2 ft. high. The sheaths and blades are glabrous, the latter having a width of ¼—½ in. and a length up to 10 in.; spikes 1—4 in. long. Native of Europe. July—Sept.

Other names: Bottle-grass, Wild Millet, Pigeon-grass.

FABERS FOXTAIL, *Setaria faberii* Herrm., a larger plant than *viridis*, from which it can be distinguished by the upper surface of the leaves being hairy and by its larger, usually-nodding heads; has been introduced from Asia.

Figure 35

ITALIAN MILLET, *Setaria italica* L. often escapes from cultivation. It, too, is larger than *viridis* with heads 4—9 in. long and the bristles usually purplish.

25a Spikelets forming a dense, cylindrical, finger-like body; bristle (awn) arising from base of flowering glume. Fig. 36............
....................WATER FOXTAIL, *Alopecurus geniculatus* L.

This moist-land, perennial grass has a height of ½—1½ ft. with leaf-blades 3 in. or often much less and sheaths shorter than the internodes; spikes 1—3 in. long. Common in our northern parts and southern Canada. July—Sept.

Other names: Marsh Foxtail, Bent Foxtail, Water Timothy, Water Foxtail, Flote-grass.

MEADOW-FOXTAIL - GRASS, A. *pratensis* L. is a similar but larger plant growing in dryer soil. It has scales fully twice as long as *geniculatus*. Both of these are weeds, natives of Europe.

Figure 36

25b Spikelets in a slender open panicle; awn, if present, terminal...26
26a Awns straight and unbranched, sometimes wanting..........30
26b Awns branched or twisted...................................27
27a The single awn twisted into a spiral at its base, 3-8 in. long. Fig.
    37.......................PORCUPINE GRASS, *Stipa spartea* Trin.

This native perennial belongs to the North Central States and plains area. Height 2—4 ft.; sheaths longer than the internodes; leaf blades 4—10 in. long, scabrous above. The grain is enclosed within the flowering glume, the sharp pointed base covered with barbs and the bent and twisted awn, 4—8 in. long, makes it a painful missle, boring its way through clothing or the hairy coat of animals to puncture the flesh. June—July.

Other names: Auger-seed, Weather-grass, Needle-grass.

NEEDLE-AND-THREAD-GRASS, S. *comata* Trin. & Rupr. is similar but smaller (1—2 ft. high). It ranges

Figure 37

from the Great Plains west to the Pacific. It differs in having the base of the panicle within the upper sheath. It is also known as Bunch-grass, Needle-grass, Silk-grass.

27b Awns 3-branched; annuals...................................28
28a The three awns of about equal length......................29
28b Lateral awns much shorter than the middle one, which is coiled at
    its base. Fig. 38....POVERTY-GRASS, *Aristida dichotoma* Michx.

A wiry, tufted, perennial grass, branching at the nodes; native annual, ½—2 ft. high; blades 1—3 in. long with sheaths much shorter than the internodes; raceme-like panicles 2—5 in. long.

Dry pastures and neglected land. Eastern North America west to Texas. Aug.—Oct.

Other names: Wire-grass, Needle-grass.

Figure 38

25

29a The 3 awns twisted into an elongated neck. Fig. 39...........
...SEA-BEACH TRIPLE-AWNED GRASS, *Aristida tuberculosa* Nutt.

Native, erect perennial, branching at the nodes, smooth; 1—2 ft. high. Sheaths shorter than the internodes; blades narrow, 6—12 in. long, scabrous above; panicle about 6 in. long.

Sandy soil; most common along the Atlantic coast and around the Great Lakes. Aug.—to Sept.

Other name: Long-awned Poverty-grass.

Figure 39

29b The 3 awns not twisted together at their base. Fig. 40.........
......................WIRE GRASS, *Aristida oligantha* Michx.

Tufted, native perennial, slender, erect, forking at the nodes; 1—2 ft. high. Sheaths longer than the internodes; blades smooth, 1—6 in. long.

Dry fields and waste places; throughout much of our territory. July—Oct.

Other names: Few-flowered Aristida, Ant-rice, Triple-awn.

Figure 40

30a Spikelets 3-flowered, the two lower flowers staminate; awn absent. Fig. 41.....................HOLY GRASS, *Hierochloe odorata* (L.)

Figure 41

Perennial with creeping rootstock; 1—2 ft. high; lower leaf blades 4—8 in. long, the upper ones much shorter; sheaths smooth; panicle 2—4 in. long, usually spreading.

A northern species common to both hemispheres and extending southward with us to Colorado and Iowa. It is a European custom to strew this and other sweetscented grasses in front of churches, hence the name. Some tribes of American Indians used these grasses for weaving. June—July.

Other names: Sweet-grass, Seneca-grass, Vanilla-grass, Indian Grass.

30b Spikelet with but one flower..................................31
31a Decumbent perennials; flowering glumes with a terminal awn or awn-pointed 32
31b Slender erect annuals; flowering glumes without an awn.....34
32a Empty glumes much smaller than flowering glumes, the lower one sometimes absent. Fig. 42....................................
..................NIMBLE WILL, *Muhlenbergia schreberi* Gmel.

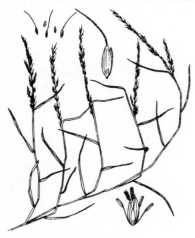

Figure 42

A very slender native perennial, decumbent, prostrate, creeping or ascending, much branched and often rooting at the nodes, with culms 1—3 ft. long. Sheaths hairy, shorter than the internodes, blades 1—4 in. long; panicles 2—7 in. long.

Common in pastures, roadsides and waste places. Aug.—Oct.

Other names: Wire-grass, Drop-seed, Satin-grass.

32b Empty glumes at least as large as the flowering glume........33

33a Empty glumes sharp pointed and about equalling the flowering
glume. Fig. 43..
..............MEXICAN DROP-SEED, *Muhlenbergia mexicana* (L.)

A much branched, usually prostrate, native perennial similar to,
but considerably coarser than the
preceding. Culms 2—4 ft. in length,
frequently rooting at the nodes;
sheaths shorter than the internodes;
blades scabrous, 3—6 in. long; panicles 2—6 in. in length.

Common in damp waste places,
roadsides, pastures, etc. Aug.—Oct.

Other names: Wood-grass, Satin-
grass, Knot-root-grass.

Figure 43

33b Empty glumes longer (often twice as long) than the flowering glume
bearing a long awn. Fig. 44.................................
...............WILD TIMOTHY, *Muhlenbergia racemosa* (Michx.)

An erect, native perennial, 1—3 ft.
high. Sheaths of the main stems
shorter than the internodes; those
on the branches longer than the internodes and overlapping each other; blades 2—5 in. long; panicles
compact, 2—4½ in. long.

In wet places. July—Sept.

Other names: Marsh Muhlenbergia, Satin-grass.

Figure 44

34a Spikelets 1/6 in. long; flowering glume (lemma) pubescent. Fig. 45.....SHEATHED RUSH-GRASS, *Sporobolus vaginaeflorus* **(Torr.)**

Slender, erect, 1—1½ ft. high; sheaths about half the length of the internodes, often inflated; leaf blades 1—3 in. long; panicles ¾—2 in. long.

A native annual growing in dry places. Aug.—Sept.

Other names: Southern Poverty-grass, Drop-seed.

Figure 45

34b Spikelets smaller, about 1/10 in. long; flowering glume glabrous. Fig. 46........SMALL RUSH-GRASS, *Sporobolus neglectus* **Nash**

Erect, ½—1 ft. high, but usually arising from a decumbent base. Sheaths much inflated, about half the length of the internodes; blades 1—3 in. long; panicles 1—2½ in. long. This species may be distinguished from the above by its smaller size and in having the flowering scales glabrous instead of pubescent.

A native annual growing in dry pastures and in waste places. Aug.—Sept.

Other name: Drop-seed.

Figure 46

29

37b Spikelets wholly deciduous; flowering glume bearing a hooked awn below the apex; upper flower staminate, lower one perfect. Fig. 47..........................VELVET GRASS, *Holcus lanatus* L.

Light green, densely covered with soft pubescence; 1½—3 ft. high; usually erect but sometimes decumbent. Blades 1—6 in. long; sheaths shorter than the internodes. Panicles densely crowded, terminal, grayish or purplish. This European perennial was introduced as a meadow grass but has become a rather widely scattered and persistent weed.

In fields, meadows and waste places. Apr.—Aug.

Other names: Mesquite-g r a s s, Dart-grass, Salem-grass, Rot-grass, Old White-top, Feather-grass, Yorkshire-fog, White Timothy.

Figure 47

38a Spikelets bearing two perfect flowers with the rachilla not extending beyond the second one. Fig. 48..........................
......................SILVER HAIR-GRASS, *Aira carophyllea* L.

Wholly glabrous and smooth, 4—12 in. high. Sheaths mostly basal, leaf blades ½—2 in. long; panicles open, 1—4 in. long, bright silvery.

An introduced, European annual of dry fields, pastures and sandy waste ground.

Other name: Mouse-grass.

Figure 48

38b Spikelets 2—8 flowered, the rachilla extending above the upper one 39

39a Spikelets drooping, 2—4 flowered; awn dorsal, long, bent and twisted. Fig. 49 . . . . WILD OAT, *Avena fatua* L.

Erect, simple, glabrous, 1—4 ft. high. Sheaths sometimes hirsute, the lower ones often overlapping, leaf blades 3—8 in. long; panicles open, 4—12 in. long; spikelets drooping.

A widely scattered European annual, especially frequent on the Pacific coast. Grain fields and in waste places. July—Sept.

Other names: Poor Oat, Drake, Wheat Oat, Haver-corn, Flax-grass, Oat-grass, Hever.

Figure 49

39b Spikelets erect or nearly so, 5—8 flowers; awn arising from between the teeth of the flowering glume. Fig. 50 . . . .
. . . . COMMON WILD-OAT GRASS, *Danthonia spicata* (L.)

Erect, simple, smooth and glabrous, 1—2½ ft. high. Sheaths shorter than the internodes; leaf blades 1—6 in. long, rough and often involute; racemes or panicles open, 1—2 in. long.

A native perennial in meadows, old pastures and neglected fields. June—Sept.

Other names: Poverty-grass, Old-fog, Bonnett-grass, White Horse, Wild-cat-grass, Wire-grass.

Figure 50

40a Spikelets set in 2 rows on opposite sides of a terminal, solitary, fruiting head 49

40b Spikelets set in two rows on the same side of the axis, flowering heads usually digitate 41

41a The uppermost spikelets terminal on the axis. Fig. 51..........
............................**WIRE GRASS,** *Eleusine indica* **(L.)**

Tufted, erect or partly decumbent, ½—2 ft. high. Sheaths loose and overlapping; leaf blades 3—12 in. long. Spikes 2—10 at top of the stem, 1/3 in. long.

An introduced annual, in dooryards, gardens and waste places. June—Sept.

Other names: Crab-grass, Goose-grass, Crowfoot-grass, Yard-grass, Dog's-tail, Crop-grass.

Figure 51

41b Axis (rachis) of spike extending beyond the spikelets as a naked point. Fig. 52......CROWFOOT, *Dactyloctenium aegyptium* **(L.)**

Decumbent with long creeping stems rooting at the nodes, culms ½—2 ft. long. Sheaths crowded and overlapping, leaf blades up to 6 in. long. Spikes 2—6 at end of stem, ½—2 in. long.

An annual introduced from Asia or Africa. Lawns, gardens or waste land. July—Sept.

O t h e r names: Egyptian-grass, Yard-grass, Crab-grass, F i n g e r-comb-grass.

Figure 52

42a Flowering glumes with 3 veins (nerves).......................43

42b Flowering glumes with 5 or more nerves.....................45

43a Lateral nerves of the flowering glume pilose; panicle open. Fig. 53
...........................TALL RED-TOP, *Triodia flava* (L.)

An erect, native perennial, 2—5 ft. high; sheaths shorter or sometimes as long as the internodes, leaf blades 4—12 in. long and up to ½ in. wide; panicles spreading ½ to 1½ ft. long, purplish red.

In fields, waste ground and gardens. July—Sept. The mature panicles often secrete a sticky substance which catches particles from the air which helps in recognizing the plant.

Other name: Purple-top.

Figure 53

43b Lateral nerves of the flowering glume glabrous................44

44a Spikelets very narrow (about 1/25 in. wide), with 5—12 flowers; flowering scales bright purplish, thin. Fig. 54.................
.............SMALL TUFTED LOVE-GRASS, *Eragrostis pilosa* (L.)

A tufted, introduced annual, ½— 1½ ft. high; smooth, slender, erect. Sheaths shorter than the internodes; leaf blades 1—5 in. long; panicles open, 2—6 in. in length, usually purplish.

Dry fields, roadsides and waste places. July—Sept.

Other name: Tufted Spear-grass.

Figure 54

44b Spikelets wider (about ⅛ in.) with 8—35 flowers. Fig. 55......
STRONG-SCENTED LOVE-GRASS, *Eragrostis megastachya* **(Koel.)**

A European annual ½—2 ft. high, usually erect but sometimes decumbent at the base. Sheaths shorter than the internodes; leaf blades 2—7 in. long; panicles 2—6 in. long.

Widely distributed in gardens, roadsides, waste land, etc. June—Sept.

Other names: Stink-grass, Candy-grass, Meadow-grass, M e a d o w Snake-grass.

Figure 55

45a Spikelets less than ¼ in. long; entire plant a low-growing annual, erect or decumbent. Fig. 56.................................
........................ANNUAL SPEAR-GRASS, *Poa annua* **L.**

A small European annual (or winter annual) 2—10 in. high. Sheaths often overlapping; leaf blades ½—4 in. long; panicles ½—4 in. long.

Common in lawns, gardens and waste places. While growing it serves well as a lawn grass but deserts the scene just when most needed, leaving unsightly bare spots. In moderate climates it may be found flowering any month of the year.

Other names: Dwarf Meadow-grass, Causeway-grass, A n n u a l Blue-grass, Sixweeks-grass.

Figure 56

45b Spikelets more than 1/3 inch long (not counting the awn)......46

46a Downy winter annual with drooping spikelets. Fig. 57.........
.................DOWNY BROME-GRASS, *Bromus tectorum* L.

A European annual or winter annual, 6—20 in. high. Sheaths pubescent and longer than the internodes; blades 1—4 in. long, densely pubescent; panicles 1-sided, full, drooping, 2—6 in. long.

Abundant on dry, sandy soil, especially along railroads and roadsides. It often seeds very early and thus perpetuates itself before normal weed cutting time. May—July.

Other names: Early Chess, Slender Chess.

Figure 57

46b Spikelets not drooping; plants glabrous or with but scattered pubescence 47

47a Flowering glumes glabrous...................................48

47b Flowering glumes with soft, appressed pubescence, neither long nor dense; sheaths pubescent. Fig. 58........................
..............................SOFT CHESS, *Bromus mollis* L.

An introduced annual, 1—3 ft. high, erect, usually pubescent, simple. Sheaths shorter than the internodes; leaf blades pubescent, 2—9 in. long; panicles 2—4 in. long, the spikelets erect, hairy.

In dry fields and waste places. June—Aug.

Other names: Soft Brome, Blubber-grass, Haver-grass, Lop-grass, Bull-grass, Hooded-grass, H a i r y Cheat.

Figure 58

48a Sheaths of leaves glabrous; margins of fruit scales inrolled. Fig. 59..................................CHEAT, *Bromus secalinus* L.

Figure 59

Introduced, winter annual, 1—3 ft. high, smooth, simple. Sheaths usually shorter than the internodes and glabrous, leaf blades somewhat hairy above, 2—9 in. long; panicles 2—7 in. long, spikelets suspended on long pedicels.

In grain fields and waste places; especially annoying in wheat and rye fields. June—July.

Other names: Chess, Cock-grass, Wheat-thief, Smooth Rye-brome.

48b Sheaths with dense soft pubescence; fruiting scales not inrolled. Fig. 60..................UPRIGHT CHESS, *Bromus racemosus* L.

Figure 60

Introduced annual, 1—3 ft. high, erect, simple and usually smooth (but sometimes somewhat hairy on lower parts). Sheaths shorter than the internodes, leaf blades 1—9 in. long, pubescent; panicles 2—10 in. long, with erect spikelets.

Widely known in fields and waste places; especially bad in wheat fields. June—July.

Other name: Smooth Brome-grass.

49a With 2 or 3 spikelets at each joint of rachis, standing with edge to rachis. See Fig. 26.......................................
..................SQUIRREL-TAIL GRASS, *Hordeum jubatum* L.

49b With but 1 spikelet at each joint of rachis..................50

50a The spikelets standing edgeways to the rachis. Fig. 61.........
...............................DARNEL, *Lolium temulentum* L.

A European annual, 2—4 ft. high, often in clumps of erect stems. Sheaths overlapping, blades 4—10 in. long, rough above, smooth below; spikes 4—12 in. long.

In grain fields and waste land; especially abundant in the West. July—Aug.

Other names: Poison Rye-grass, Cheat, Neale, Sturdy Ryle, Ivray, Bearded Darnel, Drunk, T a r e , Dragge.

Figure 61

50b The spikelets standing with their sides to the rachis...........51

51a Empty glumes with 5—7 nerves and with an awn or a sharp point; bright green. Fig. 62......QUACK GRASS, *Agropyron repens* (L.)

An introduced, European perennial, spreading by rootstocks as well as by seeds and very difficult to eradicate; 1—4 ft. high. Sheaths usually shorter than the internodes, leaf blades 3—11 in. long, rough or pubescent above, smooth on under side; spikes 2—8 in. long.

In fields and waste land, widely distributed throughout our territory. June—Aug.

It is so variable that several forms and varieties have been named.

Figure 62

Other names: Quick-grass, Knot-g r a s s, Devils-grass, Couch-grass, Twitch-grass, Witch-grass, Shelly-grass, Scutch-grass, Blue-joint, Pond-grass, Slough-grass, Colorado Blue-grass, False Wheat, Dog-grass, Sear-grass, Quickens, Stroil, Squitch, Wickens, Wheat-grass.

51b Empty glumes usually with but 1—3 nerves,—occasionally 5, awn pointed; plants bluish-green. Fig. 63...........................
............WESTERN WHEAT-GRASS, *Agropyron smithii* Rydb.

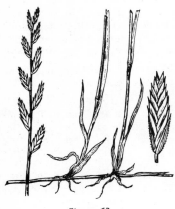

This whitish or bluish-green, glaucous, native perennial attains a height of 1½—4 ft. Sheaths shorter than the internodes; leaf blades 2—8 in. long, smooth beneath, much roughened above, standing erect and rolling lengthwise. Spike 4—8 inch long.

Grows naturally in the prairies of our Central and Western States but invades cultivated fields and is found along railroads.

Other names: Colorado Blue-stem, Western Quack-grass, Blue Joint-grass.

Figure 63

SEDGE FAMILY

52a Scales of spikelets in 3 rows or placed in a spiral; plants dark green. Fig. 64...DARK-GREEN BULRUSH, *Scirpus atrovirens* Willd.

This native, perennial sedge reproduces by creeping rootstocks as well as by seed. The triangular stems attain a height of 2—5 ft. The elongated leaves, up to ½ in. wide, are dark green and are roughened on the margins. The flowers and fruit are born in open umbels (sometimes compounded); seeds irregular, 3-angled and oblong, dull yellow.

It grows in low pastures and meadows and may become troublesome where marshes have been drained and on land subject to overflow. June—Aug.

Other names: Club-rush, Meadow-rush.

Figure 64

52b Scales of the spikelets in 2 rows...........................53

53a Plants with a small tuber at the end of elongated rootstalks....54

53b Plants with tubers basal instead of as in 52a; spikelets flat, with several to many flowers. Fig. 65..............................
..............STRAW-COLORED CYPERUS, *Cyperus strigosus* L.

A native perennial 1—3 ft. high; leaves mostly basal, about ¼ in. wide and rough margined. Spikelets flattened and borne in umbellated heads as pictured; seeds linear oblong with 3 acute angles.

Grows in swamps and low damp ground. Aug.—Oct.

Other names: Nut-grass, Ground Moss, Lank Galingale.

Figure 65

54a Fruiting heads straw-colored; achenes obovoid. Fig. 66........
.................YELLOW NUT-GRASS, *Cyperus esculentus* L.

A native perennial of 1—2 ft. or more in height. Stem simple, yellowish-green, the grass-like leaves 3-ranked, about ¼ in. wide, light green; spikelets flattened, straw-colored, many flowered and borne in umbels (often compounded) as pictured; seeds obovoid.

Frequent in cultivated fields, gardens and on sandy soil. July—Sept.

Other names: Edible Galingale, Chufa, Rush-nut, Earth-almond, Nutsedge, Northern Nut-grass, Coco, Coco sedge.

Figure 66

54b Fruiting heads dark brown or purplish. Fig. 67 . . . .
. . . . **NUT-GRASS,** *Cyperus rotundus* **L.**

An Asiatic perennial ½—1½ ft. high; leaves usually shorter than the stem, ¼ in. or less in width. Spikelets chestnut-brown, seeds oblong, 3-angled, greenish-gray to brown.

In gardens and cultivated fields, especially in the South. July—Sept.

Other names: Nut-sedge, Round-root, Coco-grass.

Figure 67

55a Perianth of 6 chaffy, scale-like, similar parts; leaves grass-like; flowers small, perfect; stamens all alike and fertile. Fig. 68 . . . .
. . . . **PATH RUSH,** *Juncus tenuis* **Willd.**

A tufted, native perennial, 3-30 in. high. Stems wiry, round; leaves very narrow and flattened, involute when dry. Flowers perfect with 3 sepals and 3 petals, green, sharp pointed; fruit a capsule-like body enclosing many tiny orange-brown seeds.

Grows in places where other plants "cannot take it" as in paths or other much traversed areas. Once established it persists to mark abandoned paths, etc. Widely distributed throughout our region and in other countries.

Other names: Field Rush, Slender Yard-grass, Wire-grass, Poverty-grass.

Figure 68

There are many species of rushes which grow in shallow water or damp places and which may persist for a time when their habitat is drained.

55b All members of the perianth leaf-like or flower-like in texture; stamens not all alike **56**

56a Plants terrestrial; leaf petioles normal **57**

56b Plants aquatic, perianth tubular at the base, leaves with inflated petiole. Fig. 69 . . . . WATER HYACINTH, *Eichornia crassipes* (Mart.)

Figure 69

A perennial, aquatic herb, apparently introduced from South America. It varies considerably in size, some plants attaining a height of 3 ft. or more. The reniform leaves have greatly inflated petioles which sustain the plant on the water. The flowers are bluish-purple and measure up to 3 in. across; they are borne in great profusion. When unchecked, whole ponds, lakes and streams in the South from Georgia to Texas may be covered with a thickly matted growth. It makes a gorgeous display but has many objectional features, however chemical sprays now make its control easier.

Other names: Wampee, River-raft.

57a Members of the perianth (petals and sepals) similar in color, size and shape **59**
57b Petals flower-like, colored; sepals smaller, leaf-like, green **58**
58a Perfect stamens 3; imperfect 3; petals deep blue, the lateral 2 larger than the third petal. Fig. 70 . . . .
. . . . ASIATIC DAYFLOWER, *Commelina communis* L.

Figure 70

This introduced annual has creeping stems measuring up to 3 ft. in length which take root at the nodes. The leaves are simple, entire and alternate on the stem, 3—5 in. long; the deep blue flowers are ½ in. or more across; each capsule produces 4 or 5 dull brown seeds.

It may be found in neglected fields, gardens, dooryards, etc. July—Oct.

VIRGINIA DAYFLOWER, C. *virginica* L., a native plant, is similar but differs in having the spathe surrounding the flower united at the base.

58b Perfect stamens 6; petals all alike. Fig. 71.....................
.................WIDOW'S TEARS, *Tradescantia ohiensis* Raf.

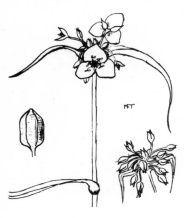

This erect, usually-glaucous, native perennial may attain a height of 3 ft. The stems are often much branched; the leaves are 6—18 in. long. The flowers, about an inch across, have 3 deep blue petals (sometimes red).

It grows in clay or sandy soil and often appears in large clumps or patches along roadsides and railroad tracks. The stems when cut weep copiously a thick sticky sap, which likely accounts for the name.

Other name: Reflexed Spiderwort.

Several other similar species are known.

Figure 71

59a Herbs with a strong odor of onions or garlic..................60
59b Plants without odor as above..............................61

LILY FAMILY

60a All leaves arising from near base of stem, flattened; bulb with a netted covering; flowers mostly replaced by little bulbs. Fig. 72.
......................MEADOW GARLIC, *Allium canadense* L.

A native perennial arising from a bulb to a height of about one foot, (the fruiting stem may be 2 ft. high). The narrow, flattened leaves arise from the base; the pink or white flowers are borne in umbels. The umbels also bear tiny bulblets often in greater numbers than the flowers.

Widely spread in moist meadows and fields. This and the following plant, as well as several other similar species, leave their objectionable flavor on the milk and butter of dairy cattle which have fed on these plants. Meat is also sometimes tainted. May—June.

Other names: Wild Onion, Wild Garlic.

Figure 72

60b Some of the leaves arising well up on the stem; leaves cylindrical and hollow; umbels erect. Fig. 73.. WILD GARLIC, *Allium vineale* L.

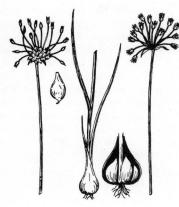

This European perennial is about 1 ft. high with its fruiting stem sometimes reaching a height of 3 ft.; the leaves are cylindrical; the flowers are purple or greenish, and like the preceding the umbels often produce many bubblets for reproduction.

It may be found in fields, meadows and along roadsides. Common on sandy soil. May—July.

Other names: Crow Garlic, Wild Onion, Field Garlic.

Figure 73

61a Flowers in racemes; leaves arising mostly from the stem. Fig. 74.
.................DEATH-CAMASS, *Zigadenus venenosus* Rydb.

This and several other similar species of *Zigadenus* are native perennials found in our western states and are notorious for causing death by poisoning to numerous sheep and also to other domestic animals and even to man. It grows from a bulb and attains a height of 8 in. to 2 ft.; the stem is unbranched, the leaves grass-like and mostly basal. The flowers are white or greenish-yellow; the fruit is a 3-lobed capsule with several light brown seeds. May—June.

Other names: Soap Plant, Alkali-grass.

Figure 74

61b Flowers in umbels or corymbs; leaves arising from the bulb. Fig. 75 . . . . STAR-OF-BETHLEHEM, *Ornithogalum umbellatum* L.

Figure 75

A European perennial, introduced as a desirable ornamental but one which refuses to quit when the game is over. It arises from a bulb to a height of 6—18 in.; the narrow linear leaves have a light midvein with dark green on either side; the flowers, white above and greenish with white margins beneath, are borne in terminal corymbs and measure somewhat less than an inch across.

In lawns, fields, meadows and unsuspected places. All parts of the plant are poisonous when eaten. May—June.

Other names: Nap-at-noon, Star-flower, Summer Snow-flake, Sleepy Dick, Eleven-o'clock-lady.

DICOTYLEDONS

1a (b, c) Corolla (petals) none; calyx (sepals) present or absent, sometimes colored and resembling a corolla. Fig. 76 2

Figure 76

1b Both calyx and corolla present. Fig. 77. (Examine a bud to be sure since some few plants drop their sepals as soon as the flowers open.) 39

Figure 77

1c Flowers of one or more kinds crowded in a head on a common receptacle with one or more rings or bracts beneath; calyx or corolla of the flowers occasionally absent; petals always united and the 5 stamens usually united by their anthers to form a tube; ovary inferior, one celled, one seeded. Fig. 78. . . .COMPOSITE FAMILY, page 153

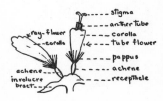

Figure 78

2a Low woody shrub, with linear leaves, appearing fern-like. Fig. 79.
..........................SWEET FERN, *Comptonia peregrina* (L.)

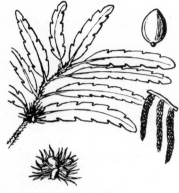

A much-branched shrub, 1—3 ft. high, spreading by creeping root-stocks. Leaves alternate, linear, 3—6 in. long and up to ½ in. wide, usually lobed as pictured but occasionally entire; noticeably fragrant when crushed. Staminate flowers in tassel-like aments an inch or less long; pistillate flowers in globular catkins, bur-like; fruit a small nut (1/5 in. shining, brown) around which are 8 awl-shaped scales.

Figure 79

This native plant grows on sandy soil and rocky hillsides throughout much of our East and as far south as North Carolina. Apr.—May.

Other names: Shrubby Fern, Sweet-bush, Fern-gale, Fern-wort, Meadow-fern, Spleenwort-bush.

2b Herbaceous plants 3

3a Leaves deeply palmately divided, appearing to be compound; flowers greenish, axillary, dioecious (staminate flower on one plant, pistillate on another). Fig. 80.............HEMP, *Cannabis sativa* L.

A Eurasion annual 3—10 ft. high with very tough fibers in the inner bark; leaves opposite (upper ones alternate) deeply cut into 5—7 narrow palmate segments 3—6 in. long, with coarse, sharp-pointed serrations. Staminate flowers with 5 sepals and 5 stamens; pistillate flower a single ovary with 2 long stigmas surrounded by an entire calyx. Fruit a smooth, rounded, yellowish-brown achene about 1/6 in. in diameter.

Introduced as a fiber crop, it has escaped to waste rich land and is widely distributed. July—Sept.

Other names: Marijuana, Hasheesh, Neckweed, Gallow-grass, Red-root.

Figure 80

3b With simple leaves...4

4a Flowers usually perfect (both stamens and pistil in the same flower). 18

4b Flowers monoecious (staminate and pistillate flowers on the same plant) or dioecious (staminate flowers on one plant, pistillate on another) or polygamous (having both perfect and imperfect flowers); ovary superior, 1-celled; fruit an achene; style or stigma one.....5

5a Plants with milky, bitter juice; flowers in calyx-like involucre with many staminate flowers (each of a single stamen) and one pistillate flower (a) (a 3-lobed pistil), the entire structure likely to be mistaken for a single flower. (Spurge Family—in part) Fig. 81 6

Figure 81

5b Plants without milky juice; flowers with a true calyx (sometimes very small) 10

SPURGE FAMILY

6a All of the leaves opposite, involucres solitary in the axils or in axillary cymes; leaves oblique at the base........................7

6b Upper leaves whorled or opposite, lower leaves scattered or alternate; involucres in a usually terminal, umbel-like inflorescence, often showy 8

7a Plant erect; appendages of the involucral glands broad and conspicuous. Fig. 82...
..............LARGE SPOTTED SPURGE, *Euphorbia maculata* L.

A rather bushy, native annual, ½—2 ft. high, usually glabrous. Leaves oblique and usually marked with red, often an inch or more long. Capsule sharply angled, glabrous; the blackish seeds 3—4 angled and marked with tiny pits and ridges.

Widely distributed in dry soil. July—Sept.

Other names: Slobber-weed, Upright Spotted Spurge, Eye-bright, Stubble Spurge, Nodding Spurge, Eyebane.

Figure 82

7b Plant prostrate, spreading, often hairy; appendages of the involucral glands minute or none. Fig. 83...................................
...........................MILK-PURSLANE, *Euphorbia supina* Raf.

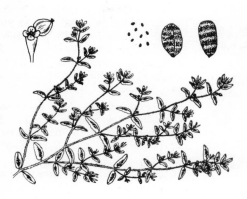

A much-branched, radiating, native annual; stems 3—15 in. long; stems usually red; leaves dark green with red blotches, ¼—½ in. long. Involucres solitary in the leaf axils, with 4 cup-shaped glands as pictured.

Common in dry or sandy soils and widely distributed. June—Nov.

Other names: Spotted Eyebright, Milkweed, Black Spurge, Spotted Spurge, Blotched Spurge, Spotted Pusley.

Figure 83

8a Involucral glands crescent-shaped; stems topped by whorled umbels.
Fig. 84...............CYPRESS SPRUGE, *Euphorbia cyparissias* L.

European perennial growing in clumps from horizontal rootstocks to a height of about a foot. Leaves very slender ½—1 in. long; those at the base of umbels whorled, the others alternate; bracts yellowish-green.

A cultivated ornamental which has escaped to persist along roadsides and in waste places; often seen in and near cemeteries. It is said to be somewhat poisonous if eaten. May—Aug.

Other names: Salvers Spurge, Graveyard-weed, Tree-moss, Irish-moss, Bonaparte's-crown, Kiss-me-Dick, Welcome-to-our-house.

Figure 84

8b Involucral glands oval, each with a petal-like appendage........9

9a Uppermost leaves petal-like, with conspicuous white margins. Fig. 85.......SNOW-ON-THE-MOUNTAIN, *Euphorbia marginata* **Pursh.**

Native annual 1—3 ft. high; upper leaves whorled, the lower ones alternate, 1—3 in. long; flowers in umbels of 3-forked branches; involucres with 5 lobes; capsules hairy, seeds grayish brown.

A wild native plant in some areas but also widely introduced as an ornamental. In pastures, gardens, fields, etc. May—Sept.

Other names: Mountain-snow, Variegated Spurge, White-margined Spurge.

Figure 85

9b Upper leaves not petal-like but the glands having broad petal-shaped appendages. Fig. 86..FLOWERING SPURGE, *Euphorbia corollata* **L.**

Native perennial, usually glabrous, 1—3 ft. high. Leaves narrow, often spatulate, ¾—2 in. long, practically sessile. Plant stem usually simple, but the top branching and rebranching in an open, widely spread umbel.

In dry soil, roadsides and waste places; widely distributed. July—Sept.

Other names: White-flowered Milkweed, Wild Hippo, Poison Milkweed, Snake-milk, White Purslane, Apple Bowman, Tramp's Spurge.

Figure 86

10a Ovary 1-celled; fruit an achene or utricle, 1-seeded..........11

10b Ovary 3-celled; fruit a capsule with 3 seeds. Fig. 87...........
......VIRGINIA THREE-SEEDED MERCURY, *Acalypha virginica* L.

Dark green (sometimes purplish or copper colored), somewhat pubescent, native annual, ½—2 ft. high. Leaves 1—4 in. long, with slender petioles and coarse serrations; both staminate and pistillate flowers surrounded by the same much-lobed bracts; seeds reddish, striated.

Common throughout the eastern half of our country, in waste places, meadows, pastures, etc. July—Sept.

Other names: Copper-leaf, Mercury-weed, Wax-balls.

Figure 87

AMARANTH FAMILY

11a Leaves entire; flowers small in dry and scarious (thin and dry, not green) axillary or terminal, spiked clusters.................12
11b Leaves toothed; flowers small, mostly axillary, not dry and scarious 15
12a Upper flowers in dense terminal spikes.....................13
12b All the flowers in small axillary clusters, usually not as long as the leaves 14
13a Each axil with a pair of heavy, sharp spines. Fig. 88.........
....................SPINY AMARANTH, *Amaranthus spinosus* L.

An introduced, tropical annual growing to a height of 1—4 ft. The heavy, somewhat-succulent stem is usually ridged, glabrous and frequently, in part, red. The leaves are 1—3 in. long; each node supports a pair of sharp spines ¼—1 in. long; the terminal spikes measure up to 6 in. long.

Now widely scattered, especially in the South, in waste places and in cultivated soil. June—Sept.

Other names: Thorny Amaranth, Prickly Careless-weed, Red Amaranth, Soldier-weed.

Figure 88

13b Without spines at the axils. Fig. 89..........................
..................GREEN AMARANTH, *Amaranthus retroflexus* **L.**

An introduced, tropical annual 1—10 ft. high. Leaves ovate to lanceolate, up to 6 in. long; flowers green, polygamous, very thickly crowded in the terminal and axillary spikes; seeds glossy black, produced in immense profusion.

Widely distributed and abundant almost everywhere. July—Oct.

Other names: Red Root, Rough Pigweed, Chinamens Greens.

SLENDER PIGWEED, *Amaranthus hybridus* L. is a similar but smaller species, darker green (often purplish) with more-slender flowering spikes. Other names are Red Amaranth and Prince's Feather.

Figure 89

14a Plants erect, branched into a rounded bush form. Fig. 90........
...........................TUMBLE-WEED, *Amaranthus albus* **L.**

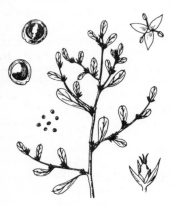

A western, native annual ½—2 ft. high. Leaves spatulate or obovate ½—1½ in. long, falling away in late summer, leaving the whitish, globe-shaped plant to break its moorings and roll over field with the wind, scattering its seeds; flowers with 3 bracts and 3 sepals.

Mostly western but often introduced locally in dry fields and waste land. July—Aug.

Other names: Tumbling Pigweed, White Pigweed.

Figure 90

14b Plant prostrate. Fig. 91..................................
................**PROSTRATE PIGWEED,** *Amaranthus graecizans* **L.**

A native annual spreading mat-like over the ground with branching stems up to 2 ft. or more in length. Leaves spatulate or obovate up to 1 in. or more in length, petioles slender and often elongated; flowers polygamous in small axillary clusters; bracts 3—5, stamens 3; seed glossy black, lens shaped.

Common in gardens, neglected dry fields, etc., mostly western.

Other names: Spreading Pigweed, Prostrate Amaranth, Mat Amaranth.

Figure 91

NETTLE FAMILY

15a Herbs with stinging hairs; leaves opposite...................**16**

15b Herbs without stinging hairs................................**17**

16a Leaves lanceolate, rounded or slightly cordate at base, nearly glabrous. Fig. 92........**SLENDER WILD NETTLE,** *Urtica gracilis* **Ait.**

A native perennial with creeping rootstocks 2—7 ft. high, with but scattered stinging hairs; leaves 3—6 in. long, 3—5 nerved, with sharp serrations and scattered pubescence; fruit a small achene.

Abundant and widely scattered across the northern part of our area in waste land and damp, rich soil. July—Sept.

Other names: Tall Nettle, Stinging Nettle, Wild Nettle.

Figure 92

16b Leaves ovate and cordate; pubescent beneath. Fig. 93.........
.............................STINGING NETTLE, *Urtica dioica* L.

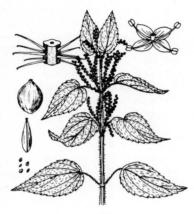

Eurasian perennial, 2—4 ft. high, thickly covered with stinging hairs; leaves 3—5 in. long and up to 3 in. wide, with 3—5 veins; flower clusters large; fruit a small yellowish achene.

Widely spread in neglected places. July—Sept.

Other names: Slender Nettle, Tall Nettle, Great Nettle.

Figure 93

17a Flower-clusters surrounded by an involucre of leafy bracts; leaves alternate. Fig. 94....PELLITORY, *Parietaria pennsylvanica* Muhl.

A native, pubescent annual around a foot or more in height. It is of weak, rather-straggling growth; leaves 1—3 in. long and up to ½ in. wide, 3 basal veins with additional branches from midrib; fruit a tiny achene.

Widely distributed; common in shady places near buildings and in woods. June—Sept.

Other name: Hammerwort.

Figure 94

17b Flower clusters in panicles or spikes, not surrounded by an involucre; leaves opposite. Fig. 95.....CLEARWEED, *Pilea pumila* (L.)

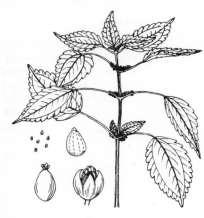

Figure 95

Native annual with translucent stem, ½—2 ft. high. Leaves very thin, with slender petioles, 3 nerved, 1—5 in. long, pubescence, scattered; fruit an ovate achene.

In damp, shaded situations covering much of the eastern half of our area. July—Sept.

Other names: Coolweed, Stingless Nettle, Richweed.

FALSE NETTLE, *Boehmeria cylindrica* (L.) a native perennial, is somewhat similar. It is larger, attaining a height up to 3 ft. and does not have the "clear" stems of the former.

18a Stipules (leaf-like appendages arising from the base of the petiole) present (in the following species surrounding a portion of the stem as a sheath). Fig. 96............................19

Figure 96

18b Weeds without apparent stipules of any kind.................31

BUCKWHEAT FAMILY

19a Calyx with 4 or 5 nearly equal lobes; stigma capitate.........20

19b Calyx with 6 lobes, the 3 inner ones enlarging to form wings on the fruit 29

20a Plants that climb by twining; leaves broad with cordate bases...21

20b Not climbing plants...22

21a Three outer sepals surrounding the mature fruit, each with a prominent wing (a); achenes shining black. Fig. 97............
..........CLIMBING FALSE BUCKWHEAT, *Polygonum scandens* L.

Native annual (or possibly perennial) with branching stem up to 20 ft. long. Leaves 1—6 in. long; flowers yellowish-green in clustered racemes 2—6 in. long; fruit a 3-sided, glossy-black achene, 1/5 in. long.

In fence-rows, cultivated fields, waste land, etc. July—Sept.

Other names: Hedge Bindweed, Hedge Buckwheat.

Figure 97

21b Outer sepals surrounding mature fruit keeled but not winged (a); achenes dull black; smaller than *scandens*. Fig. 98............
.................WILD BUCKWHEAT, *Polygonum convolvulus* L.

European annual, often branched at base, climbing or trailing up to 4 ft. long. Leaves sharp-pointed, heart shaped ½—3 in. long; flowers greenish in panicled racemes; fruit a dull black achene about 1/16 in. long.

In cultivated ground, roadsides and waste ground; widely distributed. July—Oct.

Other names: Black Bindweed, Corn-bind, Bear-bind, Ivy Bindweed, Knot Bindweed, Devil's-tether, Blackbird-bindweed.

Figure 98

22a Flowers and fruit borne in terminal spikes....................24

22b Flowers in the leaf axils...................................23

23a Plants prostrate, margins of calyx white or pinkish. Fig. 99......
........................KNOT-GRASS, *Polygonum aviculare* L.

Much branched native annual with slender, striate stems up to 1 or 2 ft. long, forming a tough mat. Leaves lanceolate and variable, often ½ in. or less but sometimes an inch or more long; fruit a reddish-brown to black 3-sided achene.

Common in paths, roadsides and much tramped areas. June —Oct.

Other names: Knotweed, Nine-ty-knot, Bird's-tongue, Cow-grass, Goose-grass, Stone-grass, Pink-weed, Mat-grass, Door-weed, Bird-grass.

Figure 99

23b Plants erect; margins of calyx yellowish or orange, leaves, flowers and fruit larger than in 23a. Fig. 100..........................
....................ERECT KNOTWEED, *Polygonum erectum* L.

Native annual, erect or ascending to a possible length of 2 ft. Leaves oval, up to 1½ in. long; sheath silvery at first, soon splitting; flowers borne singly or in pairs in the axils; achenes 3-angled, up to ⅛ in. long.

Common in yards, roadsides, etc. July—Oct.

Other names: Knotweed, Train-asse.

Figure 100

24a Sheaths with cilia on upper margin. Fig. 101a 26

24b Sheaths without cilia on upper margin. Fig. 101b 25

Figure 101

25a Flowering spikes solitary or in pairs, long and slender. Fig. 102
............MARSH SMARTWEED, *Polygonum coccineum* Muhl.

Native perennial, spreading by creeping rootstocks, stems up to 3 ft. long. Leaves 2—8 in. long; sepals 5, bright rose colored, stamens 5, style 2-cleft, both extending beyond the sepals; disk-shaped fruit dull black; about ⅛ in. across. This plant is rather easily recognized by its thickened, black roots.

In moist places and poorly drained land, highly variable. July—Sept.

Other names: Devil's Shoestring, Tanweed, Shoestring.

Figure 102

25b Flowering spikes several, standing erect; rather thick, with glandular pubescence on the peduncles. Fig. 103.....................
.....................PINKWEED, *Polygonum pensylvanicum* L.

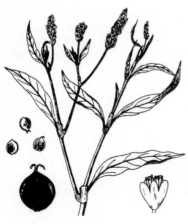

Native annual, 1—3 ft. high. Leaves 2—10 in. long, sheath thin, glabrous; spikes 1—2 in. long, dark pink or rose colored; disk-shaped fruit with a sharp point ⅛ in. across.

Common and widely distributed in cultivated ground, waste places, etc., especially if damp. July—Oct.

Other names: Hearts-ease, Purple-head, Swamp Smartweed, Glandular Smartweed.

PALE SMARTWEED, *Polygonum lapathifolium* L., also known as Willow-weed and Knotweed, is a somewhat sim-

Figure 103

ilar annual. The spikes are slender and drooping, pink or greenish white with glabrous peduncles.

26a Sheaths spreading at the border; leaves broadly ovate; spikes nodding. Fig. 104....PRINCESS-FEATHER, *Polygonum orientale* L.

Asiatic annual to 8 ft. high. Stems branched; leaves cilliate, 4—12 in. long; flowers crimson or dark rose, stamens 7, exserted; fruit a flattened reddish-brown to black achene about ⅛ in. across.

Frequent in waste places; introduced as an ornamental and escaped. Aug.—Oct.

Other names: Gentleman's Cane, Ragged-sailor, Kiss-me-over-the-garden-gate.

Figure 104

26b Sheaths not spreading; leaves rather narrow.................27

27a Sepals with glandular dots; stamens 6. Fig. 105...............
........................SMART-WEED, *Polygonum hydropiper* L.

A native annual (also found in Europe), ½—2 ft. high. Leaves glabrous, 1—4 in. long; spikes panicled, 1—3 in. long; flowers greenish, usually with 4-parted calyx, stamens usually 4 (occasionally 6); fruit dull purplish black, 1/12 in. across.

Widely distributed and common. July—Sept.

Other names: Red-shanks, Snakeweed, Water Pepper, Red-knees, Bite-tongue, Biting Knotweed, Sickleweed.

Figure 105

27b Sepals without glandular dots................................28

28a Spikes thick and compact; flowers dull greenish-white or light greenish-purple, with 6 stamens. Fig. 106 . . . .
. . . . LADY'S-THUMB, *Polygonum persicaria* L.

European annual 2/3—2 ft. high. Leaves 1—6 in. long; spikes ½—2 in. long; flowers pink to dark purple, stamens usually 6; fruit often 3-angled.

Common throughout the northern part of our area. July—Oct.

Other names: Heartweed, Spotted Smartweed, Lover's-pride, Black-heart, Peach-wort.

Figure 106

28b Spikes slender with scattered pink or clear white flowers having 8 stamens. Fig. 107 . . . .
. . . . MILD WATER-PEPPER, *Polygonum hydropiperoides* Michx.

Native, reclining perennial with stems up to 3 ft. long. Leaves 2—6 in. long, fruit a shining, 3-angled achene about 1/10 in. long.

Common in wet soil and swamps. July—Sept.

Other name: Mild Smartweed.

Figure 107

29a With hastate leaves, sour to taste; flowers dioecious. Fig. 108...
.........................SHEEP SORREL, *Rumex acetosella* L.

European perennial with creeping rootstocks and slender erect stems to 1 ft. high. Leaves as pictured, 1—4 in. long, sheaths silvery. Flowers in panicles, small, at first green then reddish or yellowish; fruit a tiny, reddish-brown, triangular achene.

In dry or sandy places; most persistent in poor, acid soil. May—Sept.

Other names: Field Sorrel, Horse Sorrel, Cow Sorrel, Red Sorrel, Sour-grass, Toad Sorrel, Mountain Sorrel.

Figure 108

GREEN SORREL, *Rumex acetosa* L., has similar leaves but grows to a height of 1—3 ft. It is now largely confned to the northeastern part of our area.

29b Leaves neither hastate nor sagitate; flowers perfect..........30

30a Leaves dark green with margins much curled and waved. Fig. 109.........................CURLED DOCK, *Rumex crispus* L.

European perennial 1—4 ft. high. Leaves dark green with crinkled, wavy margins, 6—12 in. long; flowers crowded in rather open panicles, greenish or yellowish, sepals 6; achenes shining, reddish-brown, triangular.

In pastures, fields and roadsides throughout our area. June—Sept.

Other names: Narrow Dock, Sour Dock, Yellow Dock.

Figure 109

30b Leaves lighter green, flat and with entire, regular margins. Fig. 110.............PEACH-LEAVED DOCK, *Rumex altissimus* **Wood**

Native perennial 2—4 ft. high. Leaves acute at both ends, 2—10 in. long; flowers with 6 light green sepals, densely whorled in open panicles; achenes shining, dark red.

Often abundant in low ground, in fields, pastures and roadsides. Spreads by running-roots. Apr.—July.

Other names; Smooth Dock, Tall Dock.

Figure 110

31a (b, c) Ovary 1-celled and 1-seeded..........................32

31b Ovary 3-celled and many seeded; leaves whorled, as pictured. Fig. 111...................CARPET-WEED, *Mollugo verticillata* **L.**

An introduced, tropical annual with much branched, prostrate, radiating stems forming mats 6—20 in. across. Leaves spatulate, whorled, about 1 in. long; flowers with 5 whitish sepals; seeds kidney-shaped, orange-red, shining.

Frequent on sandy soil, gravelly walks or between bricks in walks or pavements. June—Sept.

Other names: I n d i a n C h i c k weed, Devil's - grip, Whorled Chickweed.

Figure 111

31c Ovary with 10 cells each bearing a single seed. Fig. 112.......
........................**POKEWEED,** *Phytolaca americana* **L.**

Native perennial with smooth, heavy, purplish stems and fleshy, white roots; 3—12 ft. high. Leaves pinnately veined 6—12 in. long; flowers of 5 white sepals and 10 stamens, borne in a raceme; fruit at first green but becoming reddish- or blackish-purple when ripe; seeds 10, lens shaped, shining black.

In waste places. Sometimes grown as an ornamental and the seeds scattered by birds. The young shoots may be eaten like asparagus but care should be taken that no purple skins are included for that together-

Figure 112

er with the fruit and roots are poisonous. July—Sept.

Other names: Pokeberry, Scoke, Garget, Red-ink Plant, Cancer Jalap, American Cancer, Pigeonberry, Ink-berry, Redweed, Pocan-bush, Coakum.

32a Flowers with a single style or stigma, in groups of 3—5 surrounded by a 5-lobed involucre. Fig. 113.............................
............**WILD FOUR-O'CLOCK,** *Mirabilis nyctaginea* **(Michx.)**

Native perennial with angular, sometimes purplish stem, 1—3 ft. high. Leaves 2—4 in. long and up to 3 in. wide; calyx thin, red, opening in late afternoon; stamens exserted, 3—5; fruit a grayish-brown pubescent nutlet about 1/6 in. long.

Prairies, fields, roadsides. May —Sept.

Other name: Umbrella-wort.

Figure 113

32b Styles or stigmas 2 or 3....................................33

GOOSEFOOT FAMILY

33a Leaves spine-like, alternate, calyx membranous, with prominent veins. Fig. 114...RUSSIAN THISTLE, *Salsola kali tenuifolia* Tausch

Eurasian annual, 1—2 ft. high. Leaves sharp-pointed, dull green or grayish, often turning red when mature, less than 1 in. long; flowers axillary, greenish, perfect, calyx 5-lobed, stamens 5, styles 2; fruit cone-shaped. The much-branched, globular plant in late summer or fall breaks at the ground and rolls with the wind to scatter its seed.

Common in dry waste places especially in our western area. July—Oct.

Other names: Russian Cactus, S a l t w o r t, Russian Tumbleweed, Tumbling Thistle, Prickly Glasswort, Wind-witch.

Figure 114

33b Leaves not spine-like..**34**

34a Most of the flowers perfect.............................**35**

34b Flowers imperfect, the pistillate ones without sepals but surrounded by 2 bracts. Fig. 115..................................
.......HALBERD-LEAVED ORACHE, *Atriplex patula hastata* (L.)

Native annual, green or purplish, 1—3 ft. high. Leaves linear-lanceolate to broad, triangular, 1—6 in. long, flowers in interrupted panicles.

In waste places, especially alkaline soils. Aug.—Oct.

Other names: Fat-hen, Lamb's-quarters, Saltbush.

RED ORACHE, *Atriplex rosea* L. differs from the above in being covered with a silvery scurf and having rhombic-ovoid leaves is a common weed of the West.

Figure 115

RUSSIAN PIGWEED, *Axyris amaranthoides* L., a pale-green, Asiatic annual, 1—2 ft. high, with lanceolate leaves and pistillate flowers bearing 3—4 sepals, has the "tumble weed habit." It is troublesome in the North and West.

35a Calyx with 5 sepals; fruit with horizontal wings............36

35b Fruit not winged; calyx with 3—5 sepals...................37

36a Leaves with wavy, dentate margins. Fig. 116................
.........WINGED PIGWEED, *Cycloloma atriplicifolium* (Spreng.)

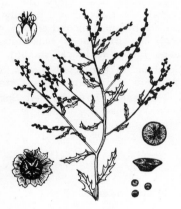

Native annual, pale green to purplish with striped angular stems, much branched, up to 1½ ft. high. Leaves as pictured, 1—3 in. long; flowers greenish in open panicles; fruit 1/6 in. broad, inclosed in a winged calyx.

A sandy soil plant of fields and waste places. July—Sept.

Other name: Tumble-weed.

Figure 116

36b Leaves entire, very narrow. Fig. 117.........................
......................SUMMER-CYPRESS, *Kochia scoparia* (L.)

Eurasian annual with slender, much-branched stems, 1—3 ft. high. Leaves pale green, 1—2 in. long; flowers perfect in axillary spikes; seeds brown marked with yellow.

Seed of this plant has been widely sold as an ornamental. It grows into an attractive, temporary hedge or symmetrically-balanced, compact, individual plants which turn red in the fall. It is a prolific seed producer and becomes a persistent weed in waste places. July—Sept.

Other names: Kochia, Broom-cypress, Burning-bush, Mexican Fireweed, Fireball.

Figure 117

37a Leaves glandular, having a pronounced odor when crushed. Fig. 118...............MEXICAN TEA, *Chenopodium ambrosioides* L.

Figure 118

Introduced, tropical, glabrous annual, 2—4 ft. high. Leaves alternate, ovate to lanceolate, 1—5 in. long. Flower spikes often leafy and arising from the axils; calyx usually 3-parted (sometimes 5) and wholly enclosing the fruit; seed lens-shaped, reddish brown to black, shining.

Common in neglected places, especially in the South. July—Oct.

Other names: Jerusalem-tea, Spanish-tea, Wormseed.

37b Leaves without glands or noticeable odor as in 37a............38

38a Sepals thick, usually with a keel; leaves usually mealy-white beneath. Fig. 119......LAMB'S QUARTERS, *Chenopodium album* L.

Figure 119

Eurasian annual with grooved stem, 1—10 ft. high. Leaves variable in shape, up to 4 in. long, often covered with a white, mealy growth beneath, but sometimes green on both sides; calyx completely enclosing the fruit; style short; seed black, shining, horizontal.

Common throughout our area in various locations. June—Sept.

Other names: Baconweed, Frostbite, Fat-hen, White Goosefoot, Pigweed, Wild Spinach.

This highly variable plant is divided into several subspecies or even species by some systematists.

38b Sepals thin and without keel; foliage scarcely if at all mealy. Fig. 120......NETTLE-LEAVED GOOSEFOOT, *Chenopodium murale* L.

Figure 120

European annual with erect or decumbent stems 1—2½ ft. high. Leaves as pictured, bright green, 2—4 in. long; flowers in small, open, axillary panicles, shorter than the leaves; calyx not wholly enclosing the fruit.

In cultivated and waste land, widely scattered. June—Sept.

Other names: Sow-bane, Swine-bane.

UPRIGHT GOOSEFOOT, *Chenopodium urbicum* L., growing to a height of 3 ft. is similar but may be recognized by the longer flower panicles which frequently exceed the leaves. It also has glossy seeds whereas those of *murale* are dull.

39a Petals separate from each other (in *Oxalis* the petals sometimes apparently slightly united). Fig. 121...40

Figure 121

39b Petals at least partly united, (very slightly in Asclepias (a); the two lower petals of most Leguminosae (b) are usually united). Fig. 122. (Many of these flowers are tubular (c))......129

Figure 122

40a Ovary superior (sepals arising from below the ovary). Fig. 123............................41
The petals of the Leguminosae are often but weakly attached to each other; such plants might seem to go here; turn however to 50.

Figure 123

40b Ovary inferior or at least partly so (sepals arising from sides or top of ovary). Fig. 124 116

Figure 124

41a Carpels distinct with one to many in each flower. Fig. 125 42

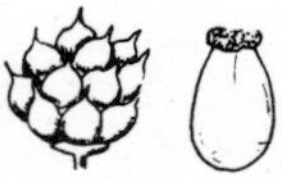

Figure 125

41b Carpels more than 1 and united into a compound ovary. Fig. 126..............................64

Figure 126

CROWFOOT FAMILY

42a Stamens usually more numerous than the sepals and arising at the base of the ovary or below it; the sepals usually distinct.......43

42b Stamens usually arising around or above the ovary, sepals usually on the edge of the cup-like receptacle. Fig. 127 46

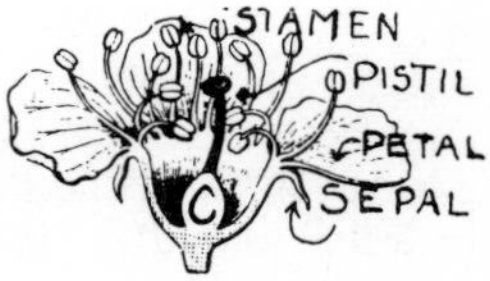

Figure 127

43a Carpels usually more than 1 (a); fruit an achene (b) or follicle (c). Fig. 128 44

Figure 128

43b Flowers with but one carpel; woody shrub with yellow flowers borne in drooping racemes. Fig. 129.....................
.....................EUROPEAN BARBERRY, *Berberis vulgaris* L.

European perennial, wood and inner bark yellow, 3—8 ft. high. Leaves 1—2 in. long, with bristle tipped serrations; 3 sharp spines at the nodes, as pictured; flowers with 6 sepals, 6 petals and 6 stamens, borne in racemes 1—2 in. long; fruit a 1-few seeded elongated berry, bright red when ripe. May—June.

This plant is an alternating host of Black Stem-Rust of wheat and other cereals and as such is a serious pest. The eradication work of the U. S. D. A. is making it comparatively scarce.

Other names: Wood-sour, Jaundice-tree, Pepperidge-bush.

Figure 129

44a Flowers regular, petals yellow.............................**45**

44b Flowers irregular, with a long spur, petals yellowish white to pale or deep blue; fruit 3 follicles. Fig. 130.......................
.....................LOW LARKSPUR, *Delphinium menziesii* DC.

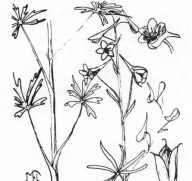

Native perennial, with tuberous roots, 1—2 ft. high. Leaves few, palmately cut, with long slender petioles; flowers perfect in open racemes, carpels 3, each producing several glossy, light brown seeds.

On ranges of the Rocky Mountains and Pacific Coast. This and several other somewhat similar members of the genus are poisonous to grazing animals. May—July.

O t h e r names: Staggerweed, Cow-poison, Peco, Poison-weed.

Figure 130

45a Petals small, about same length as sepals; basal leaves usually heart-shaped; plants glabrous. Fig. 131.........................
.......SMALL-FLOWERED CROWFOOT, *Ranunculus abortivus* L.

Figure 131

Native biennial, 6—20 in. high. Basal leaves heart-shaped or kidney-shaped, those of the stem 3-parted; flowers small with rather inconspicuous, oblong, yellow petals and many carpels; achenes with a tiny curved beak.

Common in pastures and waste places. Apr.—June.

Other names: Kidney-crowfoot, Smooth-leaved Buttercup.

45b Flowers large, ½ in. or more across; plants erect. Fig. 132......
....................MEADOW BUTTERCUP, *Ranunculus acris* L.

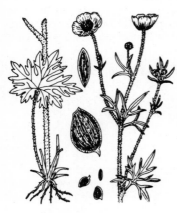

Figure 132

European perennial, hairy, erect, 2—3 ft. high. Leaves 3-divided into much-cut, sessile segments, flowers bright yellow, shining as though varnished, up to 1 in. across, petals 2—3 times as long as sepals; fruiting head globose, of several dark brown achenes. Forms of this species with double flowers are frequently cultivated as ornamentals.

Common in moist places. June—July.

Other names: Butter-daisy, Horse-gold, Batchelor's-buttons, Tall Crowfoot, Gold-cup.

BULBOUS BUTTERCUP, *Ranunculus bulbosus* L., another European perennial differs in having a corm-like, thickened base and in the leaf segments being petiolate.

PEA FAMILY

46a Fruit a legume (pea-like pod) (a); flowers usually sweet pea shaped (b) (a few are nearly regular); leaves usually compound. (Pea Family) Fig. 133...47

Figure 133

46b Flowers regular **58**

47a Flowers nearly regular, yellow; stamens separate. Fig. 134.....
.................**PARTRIDGE PEA, Cassia fasciculata Michx.**

Figure 134

Native annual, branching and spreading, 1—2 ft. high. Leaves with 20—30 leaflets and with a gland on the petiole; flowers about 1 in. across in groups of 2—4 in the axils; petals 5, unequal, yellow, some of which may bear purple spots; stamens 10, 4 with yellow anthers, the remaining 6 with purple anthers; pod usually pubescent, 1½—2½ in. long.

Roadsides etc., in dry soil. July —Sept.

Other names: Large-flowered Sensitive-plant, Prairie S e n n a , Dwarf Cassia.

SENSITIVE PEA, *Cassia nictitans* L., differs from the above in being a shorter plant and in having more leaflets (20—40) and smaller flowers (less than ½ in. across) and pods.

47b Flowers irregular. Fig. 135.................**48**

Figure 135

48a Leaves simple. Fig. 136......**RATTLE-BOX,** *Crotalaria sagittalis* L.

Native annual, villous-pubescent, erect or decumbent; stems to 1 ft. long. Leaves 1—2½ in. long; flowers yellow, in racemes of 2—4, stamens 10; pods oval, inflated, about ½ in. thick, turning black when mature; the many glossy-brown seeds become loose and rattle in the pod.

In fields and sandy soil. June—July.

Other names: Loco-weed, Wild-pea, Rattleweed.

Figure 136

48b Leaves compound. Fig. 137..49

49a Leaves pinnate, with numerous leaflets 50

49b Leaves with but 3 leaflets. Fig. 137b 54

Figure 137

50a Leaves pinnately compound. Fig. 137a......................51

50b Leaves palmately compound. Fig. 137c, 138....................
....................**LUPINE,** *Lupinus perennis* L.

Native perennial with spreading rootstocks, erect, sometimes pubescent, 1—2 ft. high. Leaves 2—3 in. across with 7—11 leaflets, as pictured; flowers ½ in. or longer, blue (sometimes white or pink), in long terminal racemes; pods about 1½ in. long, with 4-6 seeds, heavily pubescent.

Mostly in sandy soil, widely distributed. May—June.

Other names: Quakers' Bonnets, Blue Pea, Indian Bean, Sun-dial.

Figure 138

51a Leaves usually ending in a tendril. Fig. 139..53

Figure 139

51b Leaves not tendril-tipped.....................................52
52a Pods and leaves silky-pubescent. Fig. 140....................
.....................STEMLESS LOCO, *Oxytropis lamberti* **Pursh**

Native perennial, 4—12 in. high. Leaves pinnate with 9—19 leaflets, 4—9 in. long; flowers in dense spikes, arising higher than the leaves, yellow, bluish-purple or purple; pods partly separated into 2 cells, ½-1 in. long.

Dry plains and prairies, Minn. to Texas and westward. Poisonous to cattle. Apr.—Aug.

Other names: Crazy-weed, Colorado Loco Vetch, Locoweed.

Figure 140

52b Pods densely covered with hooked prickles. Fig. 141............
.....................WILD LICORICE, *Glycyrrhiza lepidota* **(Nutt.)**

Native perennial with creeping rootstocks, 1—3 ft. high. Leaves pinnately compound with 11—19 leaflets; flowers yellowish-white in dense spikes, 1—2 in. long; pods thickly covered with hooked spines, causing the scarcely dehiscent pods to cling to animals; seeds bean-shaped, dull, reddish or greenish-brown.

Prairies, meadows and waste places, Central States, westward. May—Aug.

Other names: Sweet-root, American Licorice, Licorice-root.

Figure 141

53a Style flat with beard on inner side, flowers 2—8 in elongated racemes. Fig. 142..............WILD PEA, *Lathyrus palustris* L.

Eurasian perennial, slender stems, climbing by tendrils, 1—3 ft. long. Leaves with 4—10 lanceolate leaflets and broad stipules; flowers purple, ½—1 in. long; pods 1—3 in. long, containing several reddish-brown and black seeds.

Moist fields and thickets. July—Aug.

Other name: Marsh Vetchling.

Several other similar species of this genus are sometimes weedy in habit.

Figure 142

53b Style thread-like, with a tuft of hairs at its tip; flowers 1—2, nearly sessile, in upper axils. Fig. 143................................ ....NARROW-LEAVED VETCH, *Vicia angustifolia* Reichard

European annual, with slender, climbing stems, 1—2 ft. long. Leaves with 4—16 narrow leaflets; flowers purple, ½—2/3 in. long; pods linear, smooth, 1—2 in. long.

Fields, waste land and roadsides. June—Aug.

Other names: Wild Tare, Wild Pea, Smaller Common Vetch.

Several other species of this genus, introduced or native, may sometimes persist as weeds.

Figure 143

54a Leaflets entire. Fig. 144a.......55

54b Leaflets with serrated margins. Fig. 144b 56

Figure 144

55a Flowers white or nearly so; pods elipsoid, inflated. Fig. 145......
.......**LARGE WHITE WILD INDIGO,** *Baptisia leucantha* **T & G**

Native perennial, smooth, erect and branching, 2—4 ft. high. Leaves turning black when dry, the 3 obovate leaflets 1—2 in. long; flowers white nearly 1 in. long, scattered in racemes up to 1 ft. in length; pod with a stalk twice as long as the calyx.

In pastures and along roadsides from the Central States westward. June—July.

LARGE-BRACTED WILD INDIGO, *Baptisia leucophaea* Null., a villous, pubescent plant with bracts at base of leaf, almost as large as the leaflets and with cream colored flowers, has a similar range.

Figure 145

55b Flowers rose colored to bluish-purple; fruit a loment (scalloped pod) (a). Fig. 146...
.............**SHOWY TICK-TREFOIL,** *Desmodium canadense* **(L.)**

Native perennial, pubescent, erect, 2—7 ft. high. Leaves with 3 leaflets 1—2½ in. long, flowers about ½ in. long, in crowded racemes; pod flat, separating into 3—6 adhesive parts with 1 seed in each; seeds reddish-brown.

In thickets, fields and pastures. Aug.—Sept.

Other names: Sainfoil, Canada Tick-trefoil, Beggar's lice.

Several other species of this genus, all with loment fruit and less showy than the above species, may occasionally act as weeds.

Figure 146

73

56a (b, c) Flowers in crowded, short spikes (a); pods curved (b). Fig. 147.........................BLACK MEDIC, *Medicago lupulina* L.

Eurasian annual (or winter annual), stems prostrate, becoming 1 ft. or more in length. Leaflets wedge-shaped, about ½ in. long; flowers bright yellow, very small; pods 1-seeded; seeds greenish to orange brown.

Fields, lawns and waste land; widely distributed. May—Sept.

Other names: Trefoil, Hop Medic, Hop clover, Nonesuch, Black Clover, Blackseed.

Figure 147

56b Pods straight, flowers in many-flowered heads. Fig. 148.........
...................LOW HOP-CLOVER, *Trifolium procumbens* L.

European annual with creeping, hairy stems up to 1 ft. or more in length. Leaflets about ½ in. long, the terminal one with distinct stalk but the latteral ones practically sessile; flowers yellow, 20—40, in dense heads, broader and larger than *Medicago lupulina*; seeds yellowish-green to orange-brown.

Waste land, pastures and lawns; widely distributed over our whole area. June—Aug.

Other names: Hop-trefoil, Smaller Hop-clover.

Figure 148

HOP-CLOVER, *Trifolium agarium* L., an erect plant with larger heads and leaflets, all sessile, is otherwise similar.

56c Flowers in racemes. Fig. 149................57

Figure 149

57a Flowers white; pods netted. Fig. 150.........................
.................WHITE SWEET-CLOVER, *Melilotus alba* Desr.

Eurasian biennial, growing erect, 3—8 ft. high. Leaves alternate, with usually rather narrow leaflets up to 1 in. long; flowers white, borne in slender racemes, 2—4 in. long; pods 1 or occasionally 2-seeded; seeds dull yellowish-green to orange-brown.

Often planted on roadsides to hold soil and sometimes for forage, but persists as a weed. June —Nov.

Other names: White Melilot, Honey Clover, Honey-lotus, Tree Clover, White-millet.

Figure 150

57b Flowers bright yellow; pods with transverse markings. Fig. 151..
..............YELLOW SWEET-CLOVER, *Melilotus officinalis* (L.)

Eurasian annual or biennial, 2—5 ft. high. Leaves somewhat smaller than in White Sweet-clover, and the whole plant more slender and often declining.

Used much the same as White Sweet-clover. May—Oct.

Other names: Yellow Melilot, King's Crown, Plaster Clover, Hart's Clover, King's Clover, Yellow-millet.

Figure 151

58a Herbs with perfectly symmetrical flowers (sepals, petals and carpels of the same number, or some of these parts with double number); leaves without stipules; fruit a follicle. Fig. 152 . . . .
. . . . .LIVE-FOREVER, *Sedum purpureum* (L.)

Eurasian perennial, with fleshy, tuber-like roots and stems rooting at the nodes, 1—1½ ft. high. Leaves fleshy, glabrous, with blunt teeth 1—2 in. long; flowers whitish or purplish, about 1/3 in. across in compound cymes.

This old home favorite frequently escapes to become a weed in fields and neglected places. June—Sept.

Other names: Orpine, Frog's Mouth, Live-long, Aaron's Rod, Witch's Money-bags.

Figure 152

58b Flowers with many stamens (rarely few) and the 5 petals often notched; leaves with stipules; fruit of dry achenes 59

ROSE FAMILY

59a Fruit surrounded by the dry receptacle (top of flower stem) which is covered with hooked spines; flowers yellow. Fig. 153 . . . .
. . . . . .TALL HAIRY AGRIMONIA, *Agrimonia gryposepala* Wallr.

Native perennial, thickly pubescent with minute glands, 2—4 ft. high. Leaflets as pictured, usually 7, bright green; tiny leaflets often alternating with the larger ones; flowers in elongated, slender racemes: stamens 5—15; carpels 2; the (usually 2) achenes enclosed within a dry covering, thickly set with hooked bristles.

In neglected fields, fence-rows, etc. June—Aug.

Other names: Beggar's-ticks, Stickweed, Feverfew, Cockle-bur.

Other similar species of the genus may be weedy.

Figure 153

61a Petals white, small. Fig. 154...............................
..........................WHITE AVENS, *Geum canadense* Jacq.

Native perennial, 1—2½ ft. high; basal leaves often with petioles and 5 leaflets; stem leaves sessile with 3 leaflets or lobed; sepals often extending beyond the small white petals; stamens and carpels many.

Widely distributed in woods and shaded places. June—Aug.

Other names: Herb Bennet, Red-root.

Figure 154

61b Petals yellow, conspicuous. Fig. 155.........................
..............YELLOW AVENS, *Geum aleppicum strictum* (Ait.)

Native perennial, 2—5 ft. high. Basal leaves with 5—7 leaflets, those of the stem sessile or nearly so, with 3—5 leaflets, or only lobed; petals 5, considerably longer than the sepals, bright yellow; stamens and carpels many.

In pastures and thickets, usually on low ground. June—Aug.

Other names: Black-bur, Herb Bennet, Camp-root.

Figure 155

62a Flowers solitary from the axils, on runner-like stems. Fig. 156...
...................FIVE-FINGER, *Potentilla canadensis* L.

Native perennial, mostly prostrate, spreading by runners; stems 6 in. to 2 ft. long. Leaves with apparently 5 leaflets (the outer pair on each side really united); flowers yellow with 5 petals and many stamens and carpels; achenes glabrous, yellow-brown.

Common on sandy soil in fields, road-sides, etc. May—July.

Other names: Barren Strawberry, Cinque-foil, Star-flower, Running Buttercups.

Figure 156

62b Flowers in terminal cymes, on erect plants....................63

63a Leaves with 5-7 leaflets. Fig. 157.............................
..............ROUGH-FRUITED CINQUEFOIL, *Potentilla recta* L.

European perennial, with erect, spreading stems 1—2 ft. high. Leaves alternate, palmately compound, green on both sides, somewhat pubescent; flowers with 5 pale yellow petals nearly an inch across, stamens and carpels many; achenes with a winged margin.

Frequent on stony or gravelly soils. June—Sept.

Other names: Sulphur Cinquefoil, Tormentil.

Figure 157

63b Leaves with but 3 leaflets. Fig. 158..........................
...................**ROUGH CINQUEFOIL,** *Potentilla norvegica* L.

European annual or biennial, ½—2½ ft. high. Basal leaves petioled, upper ones sessile, green on both sides, pubescent; petals yellow, shorter than lobes of the calyx; stamens 10—20, carpels many, achenes glabrous.

In fields, pastures and roadsides, usually in dry soil. June—Oct.

Other names: Barren Strawberry, Tall Five-finger.

Figure 158

64a Stamens many (more than 10 and more than twice the number of sepals or calyx lobes)....................................**65**

64b Stamens 10 or less (not more than twice the number of petals)..76

65a Ovary raised above the corolla by a stalk; corolla with a fringed crown; vine with tendrils; fruit a berry with many seeds. Fig. 159.
.....................**PASSION-FLOWER,** *Passiflora incarnata* L.

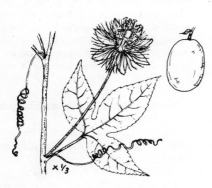

Native perennial, with trailing or climbing stems, 5—30 ft. long. Leaves alternate, usually 3-lobed, 3—5 in. across; flowers white with purplish corona, 1½—2 in. across; berry edible, yellow, with many blackish seeds attached to 3 or 4 placentae.

In cultivated fields and waste land in much of the southern part of our area. May—Aug.

Other names: Maypops, Passion Vine, Apricot-vine.

Figure 159

79

67a Leaves and stems fleshy, succulent, entire; petals 5. (PURSLANE FAMILY) Fig. 160 .... **PURSLANE,** *Portulaca oleraceae* **L.**

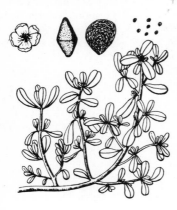

European annual, with much-branched, prostrate stems up to a foot in length. Leaves clustered at ends of branches, ½—1 in. long; flowers solitary, yellow, about ¼ in. across, open only on sunny mornings; the globular capsule opening by a lid; seeds many, black.

Very common and widely scattered in gardens, cultivated fields, etc. June—Sept.

Other names: Pursley, Pussley.

Figure 160

67b Leaves cut or lobed; juice milky or colored; flowers showy, with petals in pairs, 4—6 68

68a Leaves with spine-tipped teeth; flowers yellow or cream colored. Fig. 161 .... **MEXICAN POPPY,** *Argemone mexicana* **L.**

Annual or winter annual from Mexico, with thick stem and yellow juice, 1—2 ft. high. Leaves sessile, clasping, up to 10 in. long, often blotched with white; flowers 1—2 in. across; stamens many; pistil with 3—6 stigmas; seeds numerous, blackish brown, in a prickly capsule.

In waste land, fields and meadows. June—Sept.

Other names: Prickly Poppy, Thorn Poppy, Devil's Fig, Yellow Thistle.

WHITE PRICKLY POPPY, *Argemone alba* Lestib., with white flowers, is a rather common weed in the South and South-west.

Figure 161

68b Leaves without spines; flowers red. Fig. 162.................
............................CORN POPPY, *Papaver rhoeas* L.

Eurasian perennial or biennial, erect, thickly covered with bristly hairs, 1—3 ft. high. Leaves pinnately lobed, 2—6 in. long, the lower ones with petioles; sepals 2, falling early; petals 4, bright red, often with dark markings at base, stamens and stigmas many; seeds kidney-shaped, purplish-gray, scattering from pores at top of capsule.

In waste ground. June—August.

Other names: Corn-rose, Red-weed, Field Poppy, Thunder-flower, Cheesebowl, Canker-rose, Red Poppy.

Figure 162

69a Leaves with nearly transparent dots; flowers yellow, stamens numerous, united at their base into 3 groups. Fig. 163.............
.........COMMON ST. JOHN'S-WORT, *Hypericum perforatum* L.

European perennial, with woody base, 1—2 ft. high. Leaves sessile, ½ to nearly 1 in. long, with clear dots; flowers bright yellow, in terminal cymes, up to 1 in. across; petals with black dots on the margins; styles 3; fruit a capsule with many dark brown seeds.

Along roadsides and in waste land. June—Sept.

Other names: Herb John, Tipton-weed, Klamath-weed, Goat-weed, Rosin-rose, Amber.

Other similar native species of this genus may appear at times to be weeds.

Figure 163

69b Leaves not dotted as in 69a................................70

70a Stamens united in a central column surrounding the pistil; sepals meeting at their edges in the bud. Fig. 164 71

Figure 164

70b Stamens separate; sepals overlapping in the bud.............75

MALLOW FAMILY

71a Carpels 5; fruit a 5-celled cap-sule. Fig. 165a...........72

71b Carpels 10—20; fruit dry, the individual seeds separating from the central axis at maturity. Fig. 165b 73

Figure 165

72a Several seeds in each carpel; involucre of numerous, narrow bracts surrounding the base of flower (a). Fig. 166......................
....................FLOWER-OF-AN-HOUR, *Hibiscus trionum* L.

Figure 166

European annual, erect or spreading, ½—1½ ft. high. Leaves 5—7 lobed, hairy; flowers pale yellow with deep purple eye, closing in a few hours, 1—2 in. across; stamens many; fruit a many-seeded capsule enclosed within the inflated calyx; seeds grayish-brown.

In cultivated fields and waste ground. July—Sept.

Other names: Bladder Ketamia, Shoo-fly, Modesty, Venice's Mallow.

72b But 1 seed in each carpel; no involucre as in 72a. Fig. 167......
..............................PRICKLY SIDA, Sida spinosa L.

Introduced, tropical a n n u a l (possibly native), erect, much branched 1—2 ft. high. Leaves with soft pubescence, 1—2 in. long; petioles of the larger leaves with a spine at the base, flowers pale yellow, about 1/3 in. across; stamens many; pistil of 5 1-seeded carpels; seeds dark reddish-brown.

In gardens, cultivated fields, etc., more abundant southward. June—Sept.

Other names: False Mallow, Indian Mallow, Thistle Mallow, Spiny Sida, Prickly Mallow.

Figure 167

73a Carpels with but 1 seed, not dehiscing; involucre of 3 bracts below the calyx. Fig. 168.............74

Figure 168

73b Carpels with more than 1 seed, dehiscent; no involucre present. Fig. 169................VELVET LEAF, Abutilon theophrasti Medic

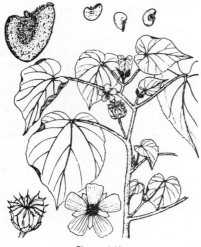

Asiatic annual with sturdy, velvety stem, 2—5 ft. high. Leaves heart-shaped w i t h long petiole and soft, velvety texture, 4—10 in. wide. Flowers yellow, stamens many, carpels 9—16, separate, each containing 3—9 g r a y i s h-brown seeds.

Common on rich or sandy soil. A most persistent weed. The seeds retain their viability unusually long, germinating after 50 years or more. Aug.—Oct.

Other names: Indian Mallow, Button-weed, B u t t e r Print, Cotton-weed, Pie Maker.

Figure 169

74a Plants procumbent; flowers axillary. Fig. 170...................
.........................LOW MALLOW, *Malva rotundifolia* L.

European annual or biennial w i t h spreading stems ½—1½ ft. long. Leaves crenate with cordate base, 1—3 in. wide. Flowers with 5 fused sepals and 5 white or pinkish, notched petals about ½ in. across; stamens many; carpels 10—20, rotating in a disk around a central axis; seeds disk-shaped, reddish brown.

Widely distributed and very common. May—Nov.

Figure 170

Other names: Cheeses, Running Mallow, Round-leaved Mallow, Blue Mallow.

74b Plants erect; flowers clustered at end of branches. Fig. 171......
.........................MUSK MALLOW, *Malva moschata* L.

European perennials, often pubescent, 1—2 ft. high. Leaves deeply lobed, 1—4 in. wide. Flowers showy, pink or white, 1½—2 in. across; stamens many; seeds kidney-shaped with concave sides, brown.

On waste — usually dry — land, regionally abundant. June—July.

Other names: Musk-plant, Musk.

Figure 171

**75a Flowers regular; petals and the many stamens arising from a fleshy ring (hypanthium) on the calyx, surrounding the pistil; leaves usually with stipules. Fig. 172. (Some other members of the Rose Family might seem to fall here; if so go to 59.)..................
............PRAIRIE ROSE,** *Rosa arkansana suffulta* **(Greene)**

Native, woody perennial, erect or spreading, thickly set with slender prickles, 1—2 ft. high. Leaves with 7—11 leaflets, glabrous on both sides. Flowers pink, in corymbs or solitary, nearly 2 in. across. Fruit a reddish, somewhat-fleshy "rose-hip" or "rose-apple" within which the bony achenes are found.

We have introduced only a very few woody plants in this selection of weeds. Several species of native "wild roses" as well as the European SWEET BRIER, *Rosa rubiginosa* L. may become a problem in pastures and grain fields. The one here pictured frequents our prairie states.

Figure 172

75b Flowers not symmetrical; sepals 4, falling off early, petals 4, leaves 3-foliate. Fig. 173....CLAMMY-WEED, *Polanisia graveolens* **Raf.**

Native annual, sticky from glandular pubescence and with a disagreeable odor, ½—1½ ft. high. Leaflets ½—1 in. long; sepals distinct, unequal, purplish; petals distinct, clawed and deeply notched, yellowish-white; stamens 9—12, purplish. Fruit a 2-valved pod with 2 placentae; seeds flattened, rough, reddish-brown.

On sandy or gravelly soil, especially along bodies of water. July—Aug.

Other names: Stinkweed, False-mustard, Wormweed, Stinking-clover.

Figure 173

76a Stamens 6 (rarely less); petals 4; sepals 4. Fig. 174.
....77

Figure 174

76b Not altogether as in 76a....................................94

77a Flowers irregular; stamens alike; leaves 3-foliate; capsule 1-celled. Fig. 175..................PINK CLEOME, *Cleome serrulata* Pursh

Native annual, with objectionable odor, stems erect, 2—4 ft. high. Leaves 1—3 in. long. Flowers in terminal racemes, pink or white, rather delicate but showy; sepals 4, distinct; petals 4, clawed. Fruit a recurved capsule on an elongated stem with many roughened, gray-brown seeds.

Common along roadsides, in fields, etc.

Other names: Stinking-clover, Rocky Mountain Bee-plant.

Figure 175

77b Stamens in 2 whorls, 4 long and 2 short (rarely only 4 or 2); capsule 2-celled. Fig. 176..................78

Figure 176

MUSTARD FAMILY

78a Fruit more than 4 times as long as wide......................86

78b Fruit less than 4 times as long as wide......................79

79a Flowers yellow 85

79b Flowers white 80

80a Partition extending from edge to edge of flattened fruit. Fig. 177a..81

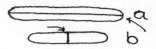

Figure 177

80b Partition extending from side to side of flattened fruit. Fig. 177b......82

81a Fruit covered with star-shaped bunches of hairs; pods short with but few seeds. Fig. 178...HOARY ALYSSUM, *Berteroa incana* (L.)

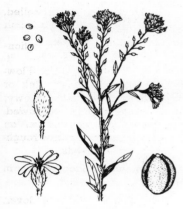

European biennial or perennial, erect or inclined, 1—2 ft. high. Leaves ½—1½ in. long. Flowers with deeply cleft petals, white; pod about ¼ in. long and about half as broad; seeds purplish-brown.

Frequents dry sandy soils. June—Sept.

Figure 178

81b Fruit glabrous; many seeds in each cell. Fig. 179..............
..................VERNAL WHITLOW-GRASS, *Draba verna* L.

European annual or biennial, with flowering and fruiting stems 2—6 in. high. Leaves all basal, covered with stiff, stellate hairs, ½—1 in. long. Flowers cleistogamous, with the petals deeply divided, pods oval, with many dull orange-brown seeds.

In dry fields and waste land. Mar.—May.

Other names: Nailwort, Shad-flower, White-blow.

Several native species of this genus are similar.

Figure 179

83a Pods wedge-shaped (a); lower leaves cut or lobed. Fig. 180.....
................SHEPHERD'S PURSE, *Capsella bursa-pastoris* (L.)

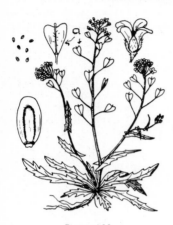

Figure 180

European annual (or winter annual) with basal rosette of lobed leaves and long flowering and fruiting racemes, standing ½—1½ ft. high. Leaves 1—5 in. long, upper ones dentate or entire. Flowers small, white or elongate pedicels which become still much longer in fruit. Pods as pictured (b), with 10—12 orange-brown seeds in each of the 2 cells.

Widely scattered and very common in lawns, gardens, etc. May be found flowering in sheltered spots every month of the year.

O t h e r names: Shepherd's-bag, Pick-purse, St. James'-weed, Mother's-heart, Witches'-pouches, Pepper-plant, Toothwort, Shovel-plant.

83b Pods rounded (disk-shaped). Fig. 181...........................
.......................FIELD PENNY-CRESS, *Thlaspi arvense* L.

Figure 181

European annual (or winter annual), erect, glabrous, ½—1½ ft. high. Leaves basal, oblanceolate, with petioles, soon dying, upper ones clasping the stem with auricled base. Flowers small, white; pedicels curved to hold pods erect; pods up to ½ in. across with 2—8 reddish-brown seeds in each cavity.

Along railroads, in waste places, etc. June—Aug.

Other names: Stinkweed, Treacle-wort, Bastard-cress, Fan-weed, Dish-mustard.

84a Stem leaves clasping; plants covered with soft down. Fig. 182...
........................FIELD CRESS, *Lepidium campestre* (L.)

European biennial or winter annual, hoary pubescent, with stems up to 1½ ft. high. Basal leaves spatulate, nearly entire, 2—3 in. long; stem leaves dentate or entire and clasping. Flowers numerous, white (occasionally pale yellowish), pods flattened as pictured (a); seeds dark brown.

Widely spread in grain fields, meadows, etc. May—July.

Other names: Cow Cress, Bastard Cress, Downy Peppergrass, False-flax, Poor-man's-pepper.

Figure 182

84b Leaves not clasping, mostly glabrous. Fig. 183.................
.................WILD PEPPERGRASS, *Lepidium virginicum* L.

Native annual or biennial, 6—15 in. high. Basal leaves often spatulate and much cut at base; stem leaves dentate or entire. Flowers white, or petals occasionally absent, stamens usually but 2. Pod disk-shaped as pictured (a); seeds chestnut-brown.

Widely spread in fields, along roadsides, etc. May—Nov.

Other names: Tongue-grass, Bird's-pepper, Poor-man's-pepper.

Two or three species closely similar to the above may be easily confused with this and with each other.

Figure 183

85a Leaves pinnately lobed; pods elongate. Fig. 184...............
...............MARSH WATER-CRESS, *Rorippa islandica* **(Oeder)**

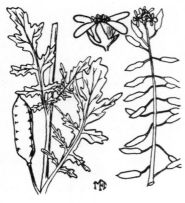

Native annual, erect, branching, 1—3 ft. high. Leaves mostly deeply lobed, the lower ones with petioles, 2—7 in. long. Flowers ¼ in. or less across, yellow; pods as pictured, bearing several yellow-brown seeds.

In poorly drained, wet ground. May—Sept.

Other names: Yellow Water-cress, Yellow Wood-cress.

Figure 184

85b Leaves but weakly toothed, upper ones auricled; pods globular
or nearly so. Fig. 185.......................................
......SMALL-FRUITED FALSE-FLAX, *Camelina microcarpa* **Andrz.**

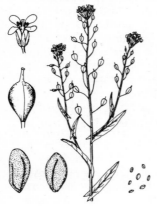

European annual, usually pubescent, 1—2 ft. high. Leaves alternate, sessile, 1—3 in. long. Racemes much elongated in fruit (1 ft. or more); flowers pale yellow; seeds several in each of the two capsules, reddish-brown.

In waste places and grain and flax fields. May—July.

Other names: Dutch-flax, Siberian Oil-seed, False-flax, Western-flax.

Figure 185

86a Fruit elongated, bead-like, indehiscent, breaking into short pieces when ripe. Fig. 186....WILD RADISH, *Raphanus raphanistrum* L.

Figure 186

European annual or winter annual, erect, branching, 1—3 ft. high. Leaves lyrate-pinnate, 2—8 in. long. Flowers ½ in. across, pale yellow (occasionally white or purplish); pod 1—1½ in. long with 3—10 seeds.

A bad weed in grain fields, etc., in some areas. July—Sept.

Other names: Jointed Charlock, Jointed Radish, Wild Kale, Wild Rape, White Charlock.

GARDEN RADISH, *Raphanus sativus* L., sometimes persists or escapes to become a weed. The flowers are pink or white and the fruit has fewer seeds and does not break into sections.

86b Fruit separating by 2 equal sides (valves) when ripe. (See Fig. 187a) 87

87a Leaves entire, cordate, clasping; flowers pale yellow. Fig. 187...
...............HARE'S-EAR MUSTARD, *Conringia orientalis* (L.)

Figure 187

European annual with slender, erect stems, 1—3 ft. high. Leaves elliptical, glaucous, rather fleshy, 2—5 in. long and up to 2 in. wide. Flowers in slender racemes, petals about ½ in. long, yellowish. Pods linear, erect, 1½—4 in. long, with grayish-brown seeds.

In waste land, gardens, etc. May—July.

Other names: Treacle Mustard, Rabbit's-ears, Klinkweed.

87b Not as in 87a..**88**

88a Leaves dark green, waxy; tip of leaf rounded. Fig. 188.........
....................**YELLOW ROCKET,** *Barbarea vulgaris* **R. Br.**

Eurasian perennial or biennial, erect, ridged stems, rather succulent, 1—2 ft. high. Leaves thickish, waxy, dark green, pinnately-divided, 2—5 in. long. Flowers bright yellow, appearing very early, ¼—1/3 in. across. Pods about 1 in. long, spreading or ascending.

Very common along roadsides and in fields. Apr.—June.

Other names: Winter Cress, Rocket Cress, Yellow-weed, Water Mustard, Bitter Cress, Herb Barbara, Wound Rocket.

Figure 188

88b Leaves not waxy; tip of leaf pointed..........................**89**
89a Flowers small, about ¼ in. across..........................**90**
89b Flowers larger, about ½ in. across..........................**91**
90a (b, c) Pods about ½ in. long, awl-shaped and closely appressed to plant stem. Fig. 189..**HEDGE MUSTARD,** *Sisymbrium officinale* **(L.)**

European annual or winter annual, growing stiffly erect with an occasional spreading branch, 1—3 ft. high. Leaves as pictured, the lower ones with petioles, upper ones sessile. Flowers yellow, ⅛ in. across.

Common in waste places, fields and gardens; widely distributed. June—Sept.

Other names: Bank-cress, Hedge Weed, Scrambling Rocket, California Mustard.

Figure 189

90b Pods linear, 2—4 in. long, often widely diverging. Fig. 190......
.................TUMBLE-MUSTARD, Sisymbrium altissimum L.

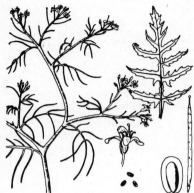

European annual or winter annual, much branched and spreading, 2—4 ft. high. Leaves deeply pinnate-divided, lower with petioles, upper ones sessile. Flowers pale yellow, valve of pods with prominent midrib.

Widely scattered in grain fields, cultivated land, etc.

Other names: Tall Sisymbrium, Tall Hedge Mustard, Jim Hill Mustard.

Figure 190

90c Pods ½—1 in. long, appressed; plant a tall, vigorous grower, 2—7 ft. high and usually quite hairy. BLACK MUSTARD, with medium sized yellow flowers, might seem to fall here. Go to 93b.
91a Tip of pod conical, without a seed in upper part. (See Fig. 193a).
...93
91b Tip of pod larger, flattened or angled, often containing a seed in the tip. (See Fig. 191a)....................................92
92a Leaves pinnately divided; pods bristly, with flattened beak occupying ½ or more of the length. Fig. 191.......................
...................WHITE MUSTARD, Brassica hirta Moench

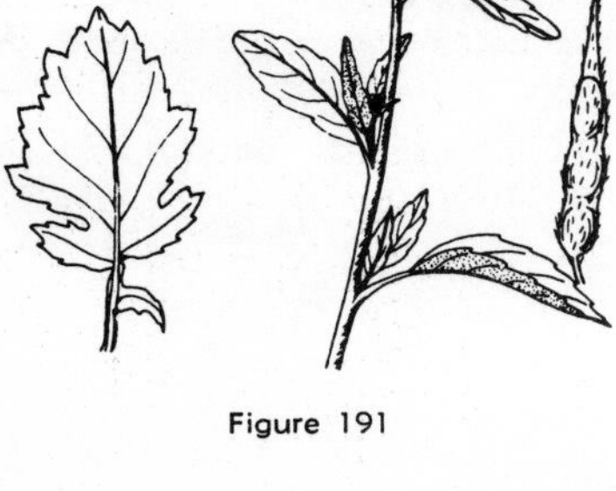

Eurasian annual, erect, with spreading branches, 1 — 2½ ft. high. Leaves, as pictured, hairy. Flowers yellow, in racemes, ½—¾ in. across. Pods with beak often longer than the valves; seeds yellow, finely pitted.

An escape from cultivation in many areas. June—Aug.

Other names: Servie, Charlock, Kedlock.

Figure 191

93

92b Leaves dentate or with lobes; pods usually smooth. Fig. 192....
.................CHARLOCK, *Brassica kaber pinnatifida* (Stokes)

European annual, erect, 1—2 ft. high. Leaves variable, 2—7 in. long. Flowers yellow, ½ in. or a bit more across. Pods with short, thick pedicels, rarely with bristles; seeds black or purplish-brown.

In waste land and in grain and cultivated fields. June—Aug.

Other names: Field Mustard, Wild Mustard, Kraut-weed, Water-cress, Yellow-flower, Crunchweed.

Figure 192

93a Pods 1—2 in. long, standing erect on pedicels more than ¼ in. long but not appressed. Fig. 193..............................
......................CHINESE MUSTARD, *Brassica juncea* (L.)

Asiatic annual or winter annual, somewhat glaucous and sometimes with sparing pubescence, 1—4 ft. high. Lower leaves with long petioles, 4—6 in. long; upper leaves smaller and often entire. Flowers yellow, ½—¾ in. across. Pods with beak nearly 1/3 the length of the body; seeds dark brown.

Widely scattered in cultivated and grain fields and in waste land. May —Aug.

Other names: Indian Mustard, Leaf Mustard.

Figure 193

93b Pods ½—1 in. long, appressed to stem; pedicels less than ¼ in. long. Fig. 194............BLACK MUSTARD, *Brassica nigra* **(L.)**

Eurasian annual or winter annual, branching, erect plant, 2—7 ft. high. Lower leaves pinnately divided, with large terminal lobe and long petiole; upper ones with fewer lobes but usually petioled, hirsute. Flowers bright yellow, ¼ to almost ½ in. across, in terminal racemes. Pods 4-sided, about ½ in. long, beak short and slender; seeds dark or light brown.

Widely distributed and very common. June—Nov.

Other names: Brown Mustard, Scurvy, Kerlock, Warlock, Cadlock.

Figure 194

94a Ovary with only 1 cell.....................................95
94b Ovary with 2 or more cells...............................106
95a With but 1 ovule (seed) in a 1-celled ovary; plants woody; leaves trifoliate. Fig. 195...............POISON IVY, *Rhus radicans* **L.**

Native woody perennial, erect shrub, up to 3 ft. high or climbing vine of greater length. Leaves as pictured, densely pubescent when young, rather variable in outline, about 4 in. long. Flowers polygamous in slender panicles 1—3 in. long; calyx 5-lobed; petals 5, greenish-yellow; stamens 5. Fruit a whitish or cream drupe, dry, globular, about 1/5 in. in diameter.

Figure 195

Along roadsides, in fence rows, pastures, etc. A serious skin poison for many people; others seem partly or wholly immune.

Other names: Poison Oak, Poison Creeper, Three-leaved Ivy, Markweed, Mercury.

The climbing form is given full species significance by some and considered only a variety by others.

95b Ovules (seeds) more than one.............................96

96a Ovules (seeds) attached to walls of ovary (parietal placenta Fig. 196a). Stamens with filliments united. (Some members of the Mallow Family might seem to fall here; turn back to 71.)

96b Ovules (seeds) attached at base or center of ovary (central placenta, Fig. 196b). Stamens distinct; leaves opposite or whorled, usually entire; stems usually swollen at the joints 97

Figure 196

PINK FAMILY

97a Sepals united to form a tube or cup-like calyx; flowers frequently showy 101

97b Sepals distinct, overlapping in the bud......................98

98a Leaves thread-like, in whorls, as pictured. Fig. 197.............
..........................CORN SPURRY, *Spergula arvensis* L.

European annual, slender, bright green, ½—1½ ft. high. Leaves about 1 in. long, in 2 groups of 6—8 each at the nodes. Flowers about ¼ in. across, in cymes, with 5 distinct sepals, 5 white petals, 5—10 stamens and 5 styles. Fruit a single celled capsule bearing many dull black seeds with narrow brown wings.

Widely distributed, usually in sandy soil. June—Aug.

Other names: Devil's-gut, Pinecheat, Poverty-weed, Pick-purse, Sandweed, Yarr, Cow-quake.

Figure 197

98b Leaves opposite, without stipules. Fig. 198....99

Figure 198

99a Fruit an elongated, usually-curved cylinder, opening by teeth at tip; styles usually 5...100

99b Fruit a short pod, splitting into valves; styles usually 3. Fig. 199..
.....................COMMON CHICKWEED, *Stellaria media* (L.)

European annual or winter annual with slender, somewhat-creeping stems, 3—15 in. long. Leaves up to 1 in. or more in length, sometimes cordate. Flowers about ¼ in. across; sepals 5, narrow and longer than petals; petals 5, deeply divided to appear as 10, white; stamens 2—10. Capsule 1-celled with many reddish-brown seeds.

Widely distributed in waste places, gardens, lawns, etc. It may be found flowering in favorable spots every month of the year.

Other names: Starweed, Winter-weed, Chicken-weed, White Bird's-eye, Bindweed.

Figure 199

100a Petals noticeably longer than the sepals; leaves linear or nearly so. Fig. 200........FIELD CHICKWEED, *Cerastium arvense* L.

Native perennial (also native of Eurasia), erect, densely tufted, a foot or less high. Leaves opposite, linear to linear-lanceolate, ½—1 in. long. Flowers cymose, ½-2/3 in. across; sepals 6; petals 5, white, rather deeply divided; stamens usually 10 and styles usually 5; pods 1-celled, with many chestnut-brown seeds.

Widely distributed in lawns, gardens, etc. Apr.—July.

Other name: Meadow Chickweed.

Figure 200

100b Petals and sepals of equal length (petals sometimes absent); leaves oblong or spatulate. Fig. 201..........................
....LARGER MOUSE-EAR CHICKWEED, *Cerastium vulgatum* L.

Figure 201

European perennial with sticky pubescence, ½—1½ ft. high. Sepals 5, obtuse; petals 5, white, 2-cleft. Pod curved upward, with many reddish-brown seeds.

Widespread throughout o u r area, in gardens, lawns, fields, etc. April—Oct.

Other name: Mouse-ear.

MOUSE-EAR CHICKWEED, *Cerastium viscosum* L., another European weed, differs in being an annual and smaller (4—12 in. high). Its pedicels are never longer than the sepals.

101a (b, c) Styles 5 (or occasionally 4)...........................105

101b Styles 3, calyx with 5 ribs...............................102

101c Styles 2, calyx tubular, round in cross section. Fig. 202.......
.....................BOUNCING BET, *Saponaria officinalis* L.

Figure 202

European perennial, spreading from a rootstock, erect, glabrous, 1—2 ft. high. Leaves opposite, sessile, with 3—5 prominent ribs, 2—3 in. long and up to 1 in. wide. Flowers pink or whitish, about 1 in. across; calyx tubular, about ¾ in. long, 5-toothed; petals obcordate; pod shorter than calyx, opening by 4 valves at end; seeds numerous, black, kidney-shaped.

Along railroads, roadsides, etc. July—Sept.

Other names: Soapwort, O l d Maid's Pink, Wild Sweet William, Sheepweed, World's Wonder, Fuller's Herb, Lady's Washbowl.

102a Calyx globular, much inflated; petals deeply cleft. Fig. 203.....
..................BLADDER CAMPION, *Silene cucubalus* Wibel

Figure 203

Eurasian perennial, glaucous, branching from base, ½—1½ ft. high. Leaves opposite, 1—3 in. long. Flowers white, about ¾ in. across, calyx at first tubular but soon becoming inflated, with prominent veins, about ½ in. long. Pod 1-celled with many gray seeds.

A frequent pest in meadows and clover. June—Sept.

Other names: Bubble Poppy, White Bottle, Sea Pink, Maiden's-tears, Devil's Rattle-box, Cow-bell, White Ben, Bird's-eggs.

102b Calyx not inflated...103

103a Stems covered with a sticky pubescence...................104

103b Stem sticky around each node but otherwise glabrous. Fig. 204..
......................SLEEPY CATCHFLY, *Silene antirrhina* L.

Figure 204

Native annual, slender, erect, 1—2½ ft. high. Leaves opposite, linear to lanceolate, basal ones often spatulate, 1—2 in. long. Flowers pink, notched at end. Seeds many, violet gray in a 1-celled capsule.

Usually on gravel or on sandy soil; widely distributed. May—July.

Other name: Terry Cockle.

104a Calyx about ½ in. long; flowers in branched racemes. Fig. 205. .
. . . . .FORKED CATCHFLY, *Silene dichotoma* Ehrh.

European annual or winter annual, erect, branching, pubescent, 1—2 ft. high. Leaves petioled below, upper ones sessile, 2—3 in. long. Flowers white with deeply cut petals. Capsule 1-celled with many dull gray, kidney-shaped seeds.

Widely distributed, preferring sandy soils. June—July.

Other name: Hairy Catchfly.

Figure 205

104b Calyx about 1 in. long; flowers in cymes. Fig. 206. . . . .
. . . . .NIGHT-FLOWERING CATCHFLY, *Silene noctiflora* L.

European annual or winter annual with heavy, simple or branched stem, thickly clothed with sticky pubescence, 1—3 ft. high. Leaves 1—5 in. long. Flowers few, white or pinkish, up to 1 in. across. Seeds gray, kidney-shaped and numerous, in 1-celled capsule.

Widely distributed on rich sandy soil. June—Sept.

Other names: Sticky Cockle, Clammy Cockle.

Figure 206

105a With large, purple flowers; the 5 styles opposite the petals. Fig.
207....................CORN COCKLE, *Agrostemma githago* L.

Eurasian winter annual with simple or sparingly branched stem, covered with heavy white pubescence, 1—3 ft. high. Leaves almost grass-like, silky, 2—5 in. long and up to ¼ in. wide. Flowers 1—3 in. across; calyx lobes 5; petals 5, purple; stamens 10; seeds black, several in the 1-celled capsule.

A pest of winter wheat. July—Sept.

Other names: Corn Rose, Corn Campion, Purple Cockle, Old Maid's Pink, Crown-of-the-field, Mullein Pink.

Figure 207

105b Fairly-large, white, (sometimes pinkish) flowers, opening at evening; styles alternating with the petals. Fig. 208...............
.........................WHITE CAMPION, *Lychnis alba* Mill.

European biennial or perennial, much branched, 1—2 ft. high. Leaves 1—3 in. long. Flowers ¾—1 in. across, white, open throughout the night but closing in the morning, fragrant; calyx tubular at first but becoming inflated and about ½ in. in diameter; petals and teeth of capsule 2-cleft. The many kidney-shaped seeds tan or gray.

In waste land, pastures and fields. June—Aug.

Other names: White Cockle, Evening Lychnis, White Robin, Snake Cuckoo, Bull Rattle, Thunder Flower.

Figure 208

106a Stamens united with each other and with the thickened stigma arising from the 2 ovaries. (In some species of the Milkweed Family the petals are scarcely if at all united and would seem to fall here.) 141

106b Stamens not in 106a...................................107

107a Stamens same number as petals or twice as many..........108

107b Stamens not as in 107a...................................115

108a Ovules and usually the seeds more than 2 in each cavity of the ovary 113

108b Ovules or seeds only 1 or 2 in each cavity of the ovary......109

109a Flowers imperfect; monoecious or dioecious; sap usually acrid or milky. Some members of the Spurge Family might seem to fall here; if so go back to 6, page 46.

109b Flowers perfect and regular; ovary 5-celled, splitting at maturity. 110

GERANIUM FAMILY

110a Leaves palmately divided.................................111

110b Leaves pinnately divided; carpels single seeded. Fig. 209......
........................STORK'S-BILL, *Erodium circutarium* (L.)

Figure 209

European annual or biennial, with sticky, villous pubescence, 6—12 in. high. Leaves 2—7 in. long and up to 1 in. wide, finely divided. Flowers pink or purplish. about 1/3 in. across, borne in umbels of 2—10 on long peduncles. Fruit dry, of 5 hair-covered carpels each bearing a single seed and a beak ½-1½ in. long, much coiled at maturity; seeds orange-brown.

Widely distributed, mostly on dry soil. Apr.—Aug.

Other names: Heron's-bill, Pingrass, Pin-weed, Wild Musk, Pink Needle, Alfilaria.

111a Peduncles longer than the leaves; carpels glabrous and smooth. Fig. 210 ....
......LONG-STOCKED CRANE'S-BILL, *Geranium columbinum* L.

European annual or biennial, slender and usually prostrate. Leaves 1—1½ in. across. Flowers with 5 petals, notched, purple, about 1/3 in. across, in 2's on peduncles 1—3 in. long. Carpels 5, each with 1 gray-brown seed.

Common in the East and in some western regions, preferring dry soil. May—July.

Figure 210

111b Peduncles shorter than the leaves; carpels hairy............112

112a Sepals awn-pointed; seeds finely reticulated; stamens 10. Fig. 211........CAROLINA CRANE'S-BILL, *Geranium carolinianum* L.

Native annual or biennial, heavy, erect stems much branched, up to a foot or more in height. Leaves 1—3 in. wide with 5—9 palmate segments. Flowers compactly clustered on 2-flowered peduncles, pale pink or whitish, about ½ in. across. Fruit hairy, seeds dark brown.

Widely distributed on poor dry soil. Apr.—Aug.

Figure 211

103

112b Sepals not tipped with an awn; seeds smooth; stamens 5. Fig. 212.....SMALL-FLOWERED CRANE'S-BILL, *Geranium pusillum* **L.**

European biennial with spreading, often-prostrate stems, up to 1½ ft. long. Leaves ½—1½ in. across, with 7—9 palmate lobes. Flowers about 1/3 in. across, pale-purple, borne in pairs on short peduncles.

Widely scattered in dry, sandy places. June—Oct.

Figure 212

**113a Leaves compound; low-growing herbs with sour sap. Fig. 213 (Wood-sorrel Family)..
...............YELLOW WOOD-SORREL,** *Oxalis corniculata* **L.**

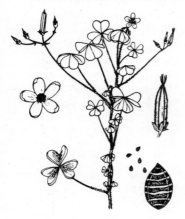

Native perennial; low or creeping, with stems often rooting at the nodes, 2—8 in. long. Leaves with 3 obcordate leaflets as pictured, on long slender petioles. Flowers yellow, about 1/3 in. across, with 1—3 on each pedicel. Fruit an oblong, erect capsule bearing several flattened, brownish seeds.

Common in waste places and on poor soil. Feb.—Nov.

Other names: Procumbent Wood-sorrel, Lady's Sorrel.

Figure 213

UPRIGHT YELLOW WOOD-SORREL, *Oxalis stricta* L., growing more erect, as well as several other species are similar to *corniculata*. These plants are often called "sheep-sorrel" but that name would better be kept for *Rumex acetocella*. (See Fig. 108)

114a Pistil with 2-5 styles; stamens attached to the receptacle; nodes of stems usually swollen. PINK FAMILY. Go back to 97.

114b Pistil with but 1 style; stamens arising from the calyx. Fig. 214 (Loosestrife Family) ....
...............CLAMMY LOOSESTRIFE, *Cuphea petiolata* (L.)

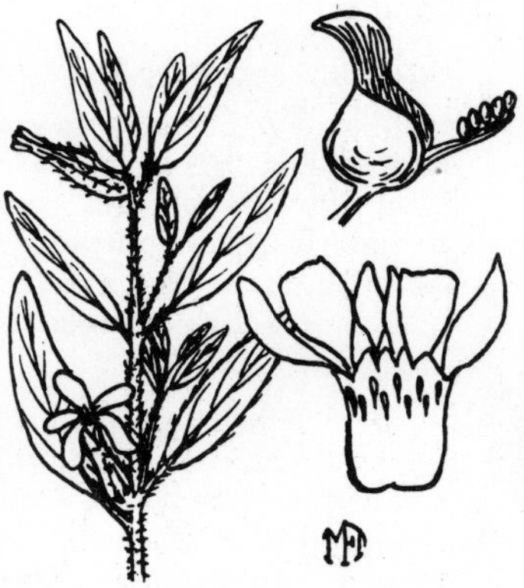

Native annual, erect, thickly covered with sticky pubescence, ½—1½ ft. high. Leaves opposite, rough, ovate-lanceolate, ½—1½ in. long. Flowers purple, about ¼ in. across, axillary, on short stems. The fruit capsule is peculiar in that it splits along one side before the seeds are ripe, the placenta then growing out of the capsule exposing the reddish-brown seeds.

Throughout the East and the South, in dry places. July—Sept.

Other names: Blue Waxweed, Clammy Cuphea, Red-stem, Sticky-stem, Tarweed.

Figure 214

115a Sepals and petals 4; stamens 6 or less; fruit a 2-celled pod (silique). Mustard Family. Go back to 78.

115b Sepals and petals 5. (St. John's-wort Family) See 69a.

116a Herbaceous vines, bearing tendrils. (Gourd Family)........207

116b Not tendril-bearing vines.................................117

117a With but 1 seed or ovule in each cell of ovary..............118

117b With more than 1 seed or ovule in each cell of ovary.......124

118a With 4 petals and 8 stamens. (Evening-primrose Family)....126

118b With 5 petals and 5 stamens; flowers and fruit usually in compound umbels ....:......................................119

CARROT FAMILY

119a Involucral bracts linear, pinnately divided; fruit with barbed prickles on the ribs; flowers white. Fig. 215..................
.............................WILD CARROT, *Daucus carota* L.

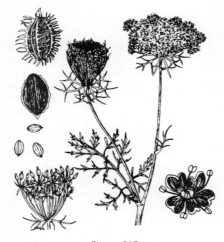

Eurasian biennial, mostly with bristly pubescence, 1—3 ft. tall. Leaves finely cut and pinnately divided; basal leaves with long petioles. Flowers white in flat-topped umbels which may measure up to 4 in. across. The central flower of the umbel often blackish-purple. As fruit matures the umbels become concave. Seeds light brown.

This wild stage of the cultivated carrot is now widely scattered and has become a highly persistent weed; especially troublesome in meadows. June—Sept.

Figure 215

Other names: Queen Anne's-lace, Birds'-nest, Devil's-plague, Laceflower.

119b Involucral bracts, if present, not as in 119a; fruit without prickles; flowers white or yellow....................................120

120a Fruit flattened laterally (a) (at right angles to the dividing line), involucre (a) dissected or with numerous bracts. Fig. 216 121

Figure 216

120b Fruit flattened dorsally (with the partition), the lateral ribs prominently winged (b); involucre small or none. Fig. 217 123

Figure 217

121a Leaves but once pinnately compounded (a); (some of the lower leaves often with leaflets much dissected (b)). Fig. 218.......
........................WATER PARSNIP, Sium suave Walt.

Native perennial, heavy-set, branched, 2—6 ft. high. Lower leaves with long petioles; upper ones often sessile or nearly so; leaflets 7—17, linear to lanceolate. When the lower leaves are submerged the leaflets are often finely dissected. (a) Flowers white, in umbels 2—3 in. across. Fruit dark brown with greenish or light brown ribs.

In marshy ground and in shallow water along streams; widely distributed. Apparently poisonous when eaten by cattle. July—Oct.

Other name: Hemlock.

Figure 218

121b Leaves at least twice pinnately compounded...............122

122a Leaflets broadly lanceolate with serrate margins. (a); roots fleshy, in clusters. Fig. 219....WATER-HEMLOCK, Circuta maculata L.

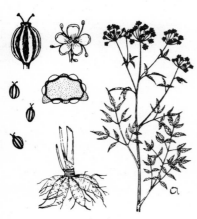

Native perennial, with stout, branching, hollow stems bearing purplish stripes, 3—7 ft. high. Leaves alternate, 2 or 3 times compound, up to 1 ft. or more long. Umbels broad, without involucre; flowers white. Seeds brown with 5 yellowish ribs.

In marshy land and along streams. Said to be poisonous when eaten. June—Aug.

Other names: Beaver Poison, Muskrat - weed, Children's - bane, Musquash-poison, Spotted Hemlock, Spotted Cowbane.

Figure 219

122b Leaflets much finely dissected; plants with a single fleshy tap-root. Fig. 220 . . . . POISON-HEMLOCK, *Conium maculatum* **L.**

Figure 220

European biennial, much branched, 2—5 ft. high. Leaves petioled below; upper ones nearly sessile; leaflets usually rather deeply cut. Flowers white, small, in compound umbels, 1—3 in. across. Seeds grayish-brown with prominent ribs when dry.

Widespread on rich soils of our northern areas. This is supposedly the "poison-hemlock" of Socrates fame. July—Aug.

Other names: Snakeweed, Poison Parsley, Wode-whistle, Poison Stink-weed, Deadly Hemlock.

123a Flowers yellow; leaves but once compounded. Fig. 221 . . . .
. . . . . WILD PARSNIP, *Pastinaca sativa* **L.**

Figure 221

European biennial, usually glabrous, 2—5 ft. high. Leaves up to 18 in. long, lower ones petioled, those at top of plant frequently sessile, leaflets broad with rather deep lobes and serrations, sessile. Umbels 2—6 in. across; flowers yellow; seeds very abundant, about ¼ in. across, light brown.

Very common along roadsides, in fields and on waste ground. It is simply the wild form of our cultivated parsnip. June—Sept.

Other names: Madnip, Hart's-eye, Queen Weed, Tank.

123b Flowers white. Fig. 222 ....
............**PURPLE-STEM ANGELICA,** *Angelica atropurpurea* **L.**

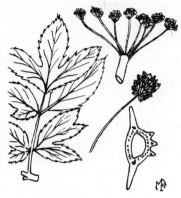

Figure 222

Native biennial, with heavy, erect, jointed, hollow stems, 4—6 ft. high. Leaves with broadly dilated petioles, the lower ones twice or more pinnately compound and very large, the leaflets serrate and frequently deeply lobed. Compound umbels sometimes nearly a foot broad; flowers white, small; fruit about ¼ in. long.

In swamps and moist places in the northern part of our area. June—July.

Other names: Great Angelica, Archangel, Masterwort, American Angelica, Aunt Jerichos, Alexanders.

124a (b, c) Spiny, fleshy plants, stems often jointed; leaves absent or small; numerous sepals and petals; stamens on a hypanthium. CACTUS FAMILY. Fig. 223...................................
............**WESTERN PRICKLEY PEAR,** *Opuntia humifusa* **Raf.**

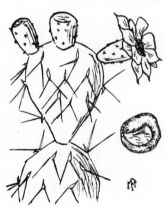

Figure 223

Native perennial, decumbent, with flattened stem-joints 2—6 in. long. Leaves tiny, awl-shaped structures at base of spines, about 1/3 in. long; spines when present ¼—1½ in. long. Flowers 2—3 in. broad, yellow, often with reddish center; petals 8—12, stamens very many. Fruit ovoid or club-shaped, fleshy, edible, 1—2 in. long, becoming reddish when ripe.

This and several other species of *Opuntia* grow in thick patches in sandy places and may become definitely weedy. July—Sept.

Other names: Indian Fig, Devil's Tongue.

124b Neither spiny nor fleshy; petals and sepals normally 5; stamens numerous on a hypanthium. (Rose Family) Turn to 59 and 75.

124c Not as in 124a or 124b...................................**125**

125a Ovary with but 1 cell; sepals or calyx lobes 2; smooth herbs with fleshy, entire leaves. See 67a, page 80.

125b Ovary with more than 1 cell (usually 4); petals 4; stamens 4—8, arising from the calyx.....................................126

EVENING PRIMROSE FAMILY

126a Flowers yellow; flower buds upright; seeds in 2 rows in each cell. Fig. 224..
..........COMMON EVENING-PRIMROSE, *Oenothera biennis* L.

Native biennial, sturdy, erect, 2—6 ft. high. Leaves alternate, ovate to lanceolate, 1—6 in. long. Flowers 1—2½ in. across with 4 yellow petal-lobes arising from the tip of a long calyx tube, opening quickly in the evening, stamens 8. Fruit a semi-cylindrical, 4-celled capsule, with many fine, dull, reddish-brown seeds.

Common in waste places, especially in dry soil; widely distributed. July—Sept. There are several similar species which may act as weeds.

Other names: Tree-primrose, Coffee-plant, King's Cure-all, Four-o'clock.

Figure 224

126b Flowers not yellow.......................................127
127a Flowers at first white, turning purplish.....................128
127b Flowers rose or purplish. Fig. 225...........................
.......................WILLOW-HERB, *Epilobium hirsutum* L.

European annual, much branched, with soft, hirsute pubescence; stem somewhat woody, 2—4 ft. high. Leaves usually opposite, 1—3 in. long. Flowers about 1 in. across, rose-purple, with notched petals (4). Fruit a linear capsule with many fine, reddish-brown seeds.

In low wet places. June—Sept.

Other names: Apple-pie, Cherry-pie, Fiddle-grass.

Figure 225

110

**128a Fruit a many seeded, dehiscent capsule; seeds in but 1 row in each cell; buds nodding. Fig. 226 . . . .
. . . . WHITE EVENING-PRIMROSE,** *Oenothera nuttallii* **Sweet**

Native perennial, usually branched, 1—3 ft. high. Leaves 1—3 in. long. Flowers axillary, the 4 broad petals white, turning pinkish or rose. Fruit 1—2 in. long.

On dry land of plains and prairies, from Canada to Mexico. June—Sept.

Figure 226

128b Fruit a single seeded, indehiscent achene; flowers irregular, with narrow petals. Fig. 227 . . . . . BIENNIAL GAURA, *Gaura biennis* **L.**

Native biennial, erect, much-branched, 2—5 ft. high. Leaves first year in flattened rosette, later leaves lanceolate, 2—4 in. long. Flowers in slender spikes, 1/3—½ in. across, white turning to pink.

Often abundant in dry soil along roadsides and in fields. July—Sept.

Figure 227

129a Calyx arising below the ovary (or surrounding its base). (Ovary superior) Fig. 228 . . 130

Figure 228

129b Calyx arising above the ovary. (Ovary inferior) Fig. 229 198

Figure 229

130a Stamens more in number than the lobes of the corolla......131

130b Stamens not exceeding the number of corolla lobes........132

131a Ovary with but 1 cell; ovules (seeds) all attached to 1 side of the ovary (pod); flowers usually pea-shaped although sometimes nearly regular. Leaves usually compound and bearing stiples. (Pea Family) Turn back to 46, page 69.

131b Ovary with more than 1 cell; stamens united by their filaments into a tube. Fig. 230 (Mallow Family) Turn back to 71, page 82.

Figure 230

132a Stamens as many as the corolla lobes and directly in front (opposite) of them; corolla lobes all alike; fruit a 1-celled capsule with few-to-many seeds. Fig. 231 133

Figure 231

132b Stamens between the corolla lobes (alternating with them) or fewer than the lobes. Fig. 232 134

Figure 232

133a Flowers yellow; plants creeping. Fig. 233.....................
...................MONEYWORT, *Lysimachia nummularis* L.

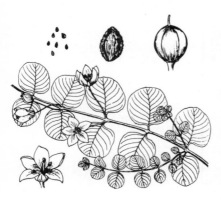

Figure 233

European perennial, with creeping stem which takes root at the nodes; stems up to 2 ft. long. Leaves opposite, broadly oval and obtuse at both ends, often cordate at base, ½—1 in. long. Flowers 2/3—1 in. across, bright yellow with dark dots. Fruit a globose capsule, shorter than the sepals, with several dark brown to black seeds.

Usually in damp places in lawns and fields. Often raised as an ornamental and escaping. June—Aug.

Other names: Creeping Loosestrife, Down-hill-of-life, Two-penny Grass, Yellow Myrtle, Creeping Jenny, Creeping Charley.

133b Flowers red, blue or white; plant not creeping, but prostrate. Fig. 234................**SCARLET PIMPERNAL,** *Anagallis arvensis* **L.**

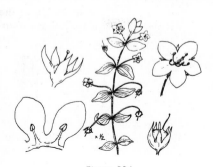

Eurasian annual with branched and spreading, prostrate stems, 4-sided and 4—12 in. long. Leaves opposite or sometimes in threes, ¼—¾ in. long; with black dots on under side. Flowers about ¼ in. across, often with darker center, opening only in sunny weather. Fruit a many seeded small globular capsule; seeds brown.

Figure 234

Widely distributed in gardens and fields. May—Aug.

Other names: Eyebright, Sunflower, Poor-man's Weatherglass, Shepherd's Delight.

134a Corolla regular (the lobes all alike). Fig. 235....135

Figure 235

134b Corolla irregular (the lobes not all alike). Fig. 236..185

Figure 236

135a Stamens the same number as the lobes of the corolla........**136**
135b Stamens fewer than the lobes of the corolla...............**154**
136a Ovaries 2, or sometimes 1 with 2 horns; sap usually milky....**138**
136b Ovary 1 ....**137**

137a Ovary deeply 4-lobed. Fig. 237..............**147**

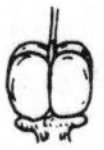

Figure 237

137b Ovary not deeply lobed. Fig. 238...........**167**

Figure 238

138a Stamens united with each other and with the stigma; styles distinct. Milkweed Family....................................**141**
138b Stamens not united; no stipules.........................**139**

DOGBANE FAMILY

139a Plants erect; fruit 2 elongated pods; seeds with hairy appendages **140**

139b Plants creeping; leaves dark green, flowers blue. Fig. 239 ......
....PERIWINKLE, *Vinca minor* L.

European perennial, trailing stems up to 2 ft. long. Leaves shining, dark green, 1—2 in. long and up to 1 in. wide. Flowers solitary, blue, about 1 in. across. Fruit 2, elongated, cylindrical follicles bearing several small, rough seeds.

Frequently escapes or persists from cultivation. Feb.—June.

Other names: Myrtle, Small Periwinkle.

Figure 239

140a Corolla bell-shaped, pinkish, in panicles. Fig. 240 ....
........SPREADING DOGBANE, *Apocynum androsaemifolium* L.

Native perennial, branching and widely spread from a horizontal rootstock; 1—4 ft. high. Leaves rather pale, 2—4 in. long. Flowers about 1/3 in. across, pink. Fruit 2 slender follicles up to 4 in. long; seeds reddish brown and bearing a tuft of white hairs.

Frequent in dry, sandy soil along roadsides and in fields. June—July.

Other names: Wandering Milkweed, Rheumatism-wood, Honey-bloom, Milk Ipecac, Western Wall-flower.

Figure 240

114

140b Corolla tubular, greenish white, in rather dense corymbs. Fig.
241.................INDIAN HEMP, *Apocynum cannabinum* L.

Native perennial, with deep, vertical root, 1—3 ft. high. Leaves 2—6 in. long, glabrous and shining above. Flowers numerous, greenish-white, about 1/6 in. across. Fruit 2 slender follicles about 3 in. long.

Widely distributed in waste land, along railroads, roadsides, etc. June—Aug.

Other names: American Hemp, Rheumatism-weed, Wild Cotton, Amy-root, Choctaw-root.

Figure 241

MILKWEED FAMILY

141a Plant a twining vine.....................................142

141b Plants with stiff, erect or decumbent stems.................143

142a Flowers dark purple, corolla wheel-shaped. Fig. 242...........
............BLACK SWALLOW-WORT, *Cynanchum nigrum* (L.)

European perennial with sparingly-branched, twining stems, up to 5 ft. or more in length. Leaves thin, opposite or occasionally whorled, 2—5 in. long. Flowers about ¼ in. across, dark purple. Fruit a pair of smooth follicles about 2 in. long; seeds flattened, brown, with a tuft of hairs.

In waste land. June—Sept.

Other name: Climbing Milkweed.

Figure 242

142b Flowers whitish; corolla vase-shaped. Fig. 243.................
.......................SANDVINE, *Ampelamus albidus* (Nutt.)

Native perennial with climbing vines 8—12 ft. long. Leaves with deep, cordate bases, 3—7 in. long. Flowers about ¼ in. long in rather dense cymes. Fruit paired follicles 3—6 in. long.

In waste land and thickets. June—Aug.

O t h e r names: Enslen's-vine, Honeyvine.

Figure 243

143a Crown of flowers bearing an incurved horn in each hood (a). Fig. 244...........144

Figure 244

143b Without incurved horn as in 143a. Fig. 245..................
.............FLORIDA MILKWEED, *Asclepias longifolia* Michx.

Native perennial, stems simple, erect, 1—3 ft. high. Leaves linear to linear-lanceolate, 2—7 in. long, usually rough to touch. Flowers about 1/6 in. long, greenish white, in compact umbels. Fruit rather slender follicles, 3—5 in. long.

In moist soil, in fields, roadsides, etc. June—Sept.

Figure 245

144a Juice not milky, flowers vermilion or orange; leaves alternate. Fig. 246..............BUTTERFLY-WEED, *Asclepias tuberosa* L.

Native perennial, densely pubescent with thick stems and many leaves, 1—2 ft. high. Leaves alternate, lanceolate, clasping or with short petioles, 2—6 in. long. Flowers numerous in umbels, varying shades of orange or rarely pure yellow. Fruit usually erect, follicles 3—4 in. long; seeds flattened, oval, ¼ in. across, brown, with tuft of silky hairs at base.

In pastures, roadsides, etc., usually in dry soil. July—Sept.

Other names: Pleurisy Root, Orange Milkweed, White-root, Orange Swallow-wort, I n d i a n Posy.

Figure 246

144b Juice milky, leaves mostly opposite; flowers not orange colored
....**145**

145a Leaves linear, in whorls of 3—7; flowers white or greenish white. Fig. 247........WHORLED MILKWEED, *Asclepias verticillata* L.

Native perennial, stem simple or somewhat branched, 1—2 ft. high. Leaves linear, sessile, 1—2 in. long in whorls, or some scattered. Flowers small, whitish; several umbels to each plant. Fruit slender follicles, 2—3 in. long.

Along roadsides and in pastures, mostly in dry ground. July —Sept.

Figure 247

145b Leaves expanded, opposite; flowers not white...............**146**

146a Leaves lanceolate, mostly glabrous; flowers rose or purplish, often with white markings. Fig. 248.............................. ....SWAMP MILKWEED, *Asclepias incarnata* **L.**

Native perennial, slender plant 2—4 ft. high. Leaves lanceolate or oblong lanceolate, 3—6 in. long and up to 1½ in. wide. Flowers rather small, rose or purplish. Fruit rather slender follicles, 2—3½ in. long.

Common and widely distributed in damp places. July—Sept.

Other names: White Indian Hemp, Rose Milkweed, Water-nerve-root.

Figure 248

146b Leaves broadly oval, with pale pubescence beneath, occasionally whorled; flowers greenish purple. Fig. 249.................... ....COMMON MILKWEED, *Asclepias syriaca* **L.**

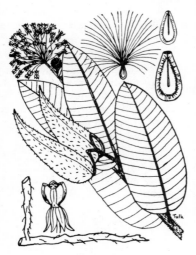

Native perennial with heavy stem, 2½—5 ft. high. Leaves oblong or oval, 4—8 in. long and 2—4 in. wide. Flowers greenish purple to greenish white. Fruit paired follicles, 3—5 in. long and covered with soft horn like processes. Seeds much flattened, brown, with tuft of silky white hairs.

Abundant in fields, especially in grain. June—Aug.

Other names: Silkweed, Cotton-weed, Wild Cotton, Virginia Silk.

Figure 249

147a Leaves alternate; flowers often blue, though sometimes yellow, red or other colors.......................................148

147b Leaves opposite; stems usually square in cross section. MINT FAMILY 158

BORAGE FAMILY

148a Flowers regular 149

148b Flowers somewhat irregular; stamens unequal and extending beyond the corolla; flowers blue. Fig. 250......................
..........................BLUE THISTLE, *Echium vulgare* L.

European biennial, bristly-hispid, branching, 1—2½ ft. high. Leaves linear-lanceolate, 2—6 in. long. Flowers bright blue (buds pink), up to 1 in. long; the 5 stamens attached to the wall of the corolla; anthers red. Fruit 4 3-angled nutlets, rough but without prickles.

Widely distributed on dry, sandy or stony soil. June—July.

Other names: Blue Devil, Viper's-grass, Blue-weed, S n a k e Flower, Viper's Bugloss, Cat's-tails.

Figure 250

149a Fruit covered with barbed prickles; flowers red, purplish or blue. Fig. 251 150

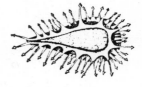

Figure 251

149b Fruit without barbed prickles and either smooth or roughened..151

150a The 4 nutlets diverging from each other; the prickles covering the whole surface; flowers deep red or purplish. Fig. 252......
..................HOUND'S-TONGUE, *Cynoglossum officinale* L.

European biennial, pubescent, erect, with many leaves, 1—3 ft. high. Leaves 3—12 in. long, ½—3 in. wide, deep green. Flowers in terminal racemes; corolla deep red or reddish purple (rarely white), about 1/3 in. across. Fruit brown; nutlets about ¼ in. across.

Frequent in pastures and waste places, eastern half of our region. May—Aug.

Other names: Sheep-lice, Dog-bur, Gipsy Flower, Wood-mat, Rose-noble, Tory-weed.

Figure 252

150b The 4 nutlets standing erect and close together; prickles thickest along the margins; flowers blue. Fig. 253...................
..........................STICKSEED, *Lappula echinata* Gilib.

Eurasian a n n u a l, pubescent, branching, 1—2 ft. high. Leaves linear, rather erect, ½—1½ in. long, pale green. Flowers blue, small, in bracted, terminal racemes. Fruit 4 nutlets attached along the sides, ⅛ in. or less long, grayish brown.

In waste land and pastures. May—Aug.

Other names: Burseed, Sheep-bur, Stick-tight, Blue-bur.

Figure 253

151a Nutlets smooth or nearly so; flowers whitish, pinkish or purplish 152

151b Nutlets roughened, flowers orange-yellow. Fig. 254 ....
.......................TARWEED, *Amsinckia intermedia* F. & M.

Figure 254

Californian a n n u a l , erect, branching and thickly covered with bristly hairs, 1—2½ ft. high. Leaves linear, 1—4 in. long. Flowers yellow, about ¼ in. long, in coiled and greatly elongating racemes. Fruit roughened, with wrinkles but without prickles, gray-brown.

Scattered in fields and waste places in eastern half of our area. May—July.

Other names: Yellow Forget-me-not, Buckthorn Weed, Finger-weed, Fireweed.

Amsinckia barbata Greene, a decumbent annual is similar to the above in most other ways.

152a Corolla funnel-shaped, white or yellowish white, ¼ in. or less in length 153

152b Corolla tubular, its throat closed, yellowish- or pinkish-white or purplish, ½—¾ in. long. Fig. 255 ....
.......................COMFREY, *Symphytum officinale* L.

Figure 255

Eurasian perennial, pubescent, from deep, thickened roots, 2—3 ft. high. Leaves alternate, 3—12 in. long. Flowers numerous in dense racemes. Fruit 4 erect, brown nutlets, nearly smooth and somewhat shining.

In moist waste places. Originally introduced as a medicinal herb. June—Aug.

Other names: Healing Herb, Bruisewort, Backwort, Gum-plant, Boneset, Knitback.

153a Nutlets white, smooth, shining; plant 2 ft. or more high. Fig. 256
..................PEARL PLANT, *Lithospermum officinale* L.

Eurasian perennial, much branched, grayish, 2—4 ft. high. Leaves 1-4 in. long and up to 1 in. wide, with roughened upper surface. Flowers about 1/12 in. long, yellowish-white, with crest in throat. Fruit, 4 shining, ivory-white nutlets.

In waste ground, preferring limestone areas. June—Aug.

Other names: Graymile, Littlewale, Gromwell.

Figure 256

153b Nutlets brownish and dull, somewhat wrinkled and pitted; plant less than 2 ft. high. Fig. 257...................................
..................CORN GROMWELL, *Lithospermum arvense* L.

European biennial or winter annual, with appressed pubescence; ½—1½ ft. high. Leaves narrow, bright green, up to 3 in. long. Flowers white, about ¼ in. long, corolla with crest. Fruit, 4 dull brown nutlets.

In waste land, widely distributed. May—Aug.

Other names: Wheat-thief, Redroot, Pigeon-weed, Stone-seed, Bastard Alkanet.

Figure 257

154a Fertile stamens only 2; herbs with leaves arising at or near the ground 194
154b Fertile stamens 4, in 2 pairs; ovary with 2 or 4 cells and with but 1 seed to each cell...................................155

VERBENA FAMILY

155a Plants growing erect; flowering spikes slender............156
155b Plants decumbent in dense mats over the ground; flowering spikes with long bracts, thickened. Fig. 258........................
...........**BRACTED VERVAIN**, *Verbena bracteata* Lag. & Rodr.

Native annual, heavily pubescent, the 4-sided stems mostly decumbent with the ends turning upward. ½—1½ ft. long. Leaves, as pictured, 1—3 in. long. Flowers 1/10 in. or less across, purplish blue, in long-bracted, dense spikes, becoming 3—6 in. long. Seeds dark brown with a white scar.

Widely distributed in waste land. Often takes over part of a barnyard. May—Sept.

Other name: Prostrate Vervain.

Figure 258

156a Leaves harsh and sometimes pubescent, but not downy; petioled; flowers small, ⅛ in. or less across........................157
156b Leaves thickly covered with rather long white hairs, sessile; flowers 1/3 in. or more across, blue or purple (rarely white or pink). Fig. 259..............**HOARY VERVAIN**, *Verbena stricta* Vent.

Native perennial, heavy, 4-angled, sparingly-branched stem 1—2½ ft. high. Leaves sessile, 1—4 in. long, thickly clothed with white hairs. Flowers purplish-blue (occasional albinos) in long dense spikes, becoming up to a foot in length. Fruit with 4 dark brown seeds.

Common in pastures and fields. June—Sept.

Other names: Woolly Vervain, Mullein-leaved Vervain.

Figure 259

157a Flowers white; spikes very slender with fruits scattered on the stem. Fig. 260 . . . . WHITE VERVAIN, *Verbena urticifolia* L.

Native perennial with rather slender, 4-sided erect stems, 3—5 ft. high. Leaves serrate-dentate, 1—5 in. long. Flowers 1/10 in. across in numerous long spikes, white (rarely pale blue or purplish). Nutlets small reddish-brown.

Common in pastures, fields and waste land. June—Sept.

Other name: Netted-leaved Vervain.

Figure 260

157b Flowers purplish-blue, fruits crowded on the spikes. Fig. 261 . . . . BLUE VERVAIN, *Verbena hastata* L.

Native perennial, erect, somewhat branched, stem 4-sided, 3—7 ft. high. Leaves oblong lanceolate or narrower, rough, 2—6 in. long. Flowers about ⅛ in. across, usually blue but occasionally white or pink. Fruit crowded on the spike, nutlets reddish-brown.

Common in moist places. June —Sept.

Other names: Wild Hyssop, False Vervain, Ironweed, Simpler's-joy.

Figure 261

MINT FAMILY

158a Style and stamens not reaching beyond the coralla tube; calyx teeth ending in a recurved bristle; plant woolly. Fig. 262......
..............COMMON HOARHOUND, *Marrubium vulgare* L.

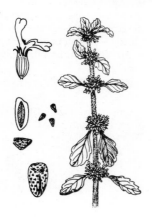

European perennial, thickly covered with white wool, 1—3 ft. high. Leaves oval or orbicular, whitish a b o v e, wool-covered beneath, 1—2 in. long. Flowers white, in dense axillary clusters; calyx with 10 recurving teeth. Fruit 4 grayish-brown nutlets marked with darker granules.

Widely scattered in waste land. June—Aug.

O t h e r names: Houndsbane, W h i t e Hoarhound, Marrube.

Figure 262

158b Stamens reaching beyond the corolla tube, and otherwise not as in 158a 159
159a Anther-bearing stamens 4..................................161
159b Anther-bearing stamens but 2.............................160
160a Upper lip of corolla long and concave; flowers in dense terminal heads. Fig. 263........WILD BERGAMOT, *Monarda fistulosa* L.

Native perennial, smooth or pubescent, 2—3 ft. high. Leaves thin, 1—4 in. long. Flowers 1—1½ in. long, pinkish, lilac or purplish (rarely white).

Very common on dry hillsides and in pastures, the stems and leaves often with purplish tints. June—Sept.

Other name: Horse Mint.

Figure 263

160b Upper lip of corolla shorter and rounded; flowers in axillary clusters. Fig. 264 . . . .
. . . . AMERICAN PENNYROYAL, *Hedeoma pulegioides* (L.)

Native annual, finely pubescent, very slender, erect, much branched, ½—1½ ft. high. Leaves as pictured, thin, ½—1½ in. long. Flowers bluish-purple, about ¼ in. long. Fruit 4 small blackish nutlets.

Frequent in dry pastures and meadows. July—Sept.

Other names: Stinking Balm, Mock Pennyroyal, Squaw-mint, Tickweed.

Figure 264

161a Corolla two lipped. Fig. 265 162

Figure 265

161b Corolla regular or nearly so; flowers in slender terminal spikes; leaves sessile. Fig. 266 . . . . SPEARMINT, *Mentha spicata* L.

Eurasian perennial, spreading vigorously from creeping rootstocks, 1—1½ ft. high. Leaves opposite, usually sessile, ½—1½ in. long. Flowers, white to pale lavender, in elongated interrupted spikes. Seeds apparently seldom, if ever, mature in this country, the plant spreading solely by means of its rootstalks.

Frequent as an escape from cultivation. July—Sept.

Other names: Garden Mint, Lamb Mint, Sage-of-Bethlehem, Our Lady's Mint.

Figure 266

Several other species of the genus, PEPPERMINT, *Mentha piperita* L., CORN MINT, *Mentha arvensis* L. and CREEPING WHORLED MINT, *Mentha gentilis* L., all sometimes act as weeds.

162a The upper pair of stamens shorter than the lower ones......164

162b The upper pair of stamens longer than the lower ones......163

163a Plant erect, calyx 5-toothed, not two lipped. Fig. 267..........
............................CATNIP, *Nepeta cataria* L.

Eurasian perennial, pale green with dense canescence, erect, branched, 2—3 ft. high. Leaves 1—3 in. long, frequently with cordate base. Flowers about ½ in. long, white or pale lavender with dark dots, in elongate terminal spikes. Nutlets dark reddish-brown with 2 white spots near base.

Widely distributed on rich soil. July—Sept.

Other name: Catmint.

Figure 267

163b Plants creeping; leaves orbicular or reniform. Fig. 268........
........................GROUND IVY, *Glechoma hederaceae* L.

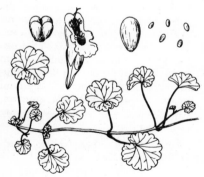

Eurasian perenial, with creeping stems up to 18 in. or longer. Leaves with long petioles, deep green, ¾—1½ in. across. Flowers clustered in the axils, bluish-purple, ½—¾ in. long. Nutlets dark brown with white spot at base.

Often thickly matted in damp shaded places. April—June.

Other names: Gill - over - the - ground, Field Balm, Creeping Charlie, Cat's - foot, Run - away - Robin.

Figure 268

164a Calyx nearly regular, not 2-lipped; open in fruit............165

164b Calyx definitely 2-lipped; closed in fruit. Fig. 269..............
.............................HEAL-ALL, *Prunella vulgaris* L.

Native perennial, with short root-stocks, procumbent or ascending with stems up to 2 ft. long. Leaves variable 1—4 in. long. Flowers violet-purple (rarely white), 1/3—½ in. long in terminal spikes, lengthening to 2—4 in. in fruit.

Widely distributed in pastures, meadows and waste land. June—Sept.

Other names: Self-heal, Carpenter's-weed, Thimble-flower, Heart-of-the-earth.

Figure 269

165a Calyx teeth tipped with spines...........................166

165b Calyx teeth not spined; upper leaves sessile and clasping. Fig. 270...........................HENBIT, *Lamium amplexicaule* L.

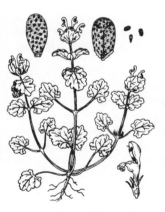

Eurasian biennial or winter annual with slender ascending or decumbent stems up to 1½ ft. long. Leaves orbicular ½—1½ in. across, the lower ones with slender petioles. Flowers purplish or red, some of them producing seed without opening. Nutlets 3-angled, brown, specked with silver-gray.

In gardens and rich waste land. Feb.—Oct.

Other names: Bee Nettle, Dead Nettle, Blind Nettle.

Two other Eurasian members of the genus are found in our weed flora; RED DEAD NETTLE, *Lamium purpureum* L. differs in having its upper leaves petioled while variegated.

Figure 270

DEAD NETTLE, *Lamium maculatum* L., has blotched leaves and flowers 1 in. long.

166a Flowers 2/3—1 in. long; anthers opening transversely. Fig. 271..
........................HEMP NETTLE, *Galeopsis tetrahit* L.

European annual, with erect spreading stems 1—3 ft. high. Leaves coarsely dentate, 2—5 in. long.

Flowers pale purple or pink with white markings, in axillary clusters. Nutlets with one side convex, the other angled.

Found on cultivated ground and waste places. July—Sept.

Other names: Dog Nettle, Wild Hemp, Ironwort, Simon's-weed.

Figure 271

166b Flowers less than ½ in. long; anther sacs parallel with the fila-
ment. Fig. 272............MOTHERWORT, *Leonurus cardiaca* L.

European perennial; erect sturdy stem 2—5 ft. high. Leaves thin; upper ones narrow with three lobes, lower ones broader (2—4 in.) and 5-cleft. Flowers about 1/3 in. long, numerous in many axillary clusters, pink, purple or occasionally white. Nutlets 3-angled, dark brown.

Common in fields, roadsides and waste places. July—Sept.

Other names: Lion's-ear, Lion's-tail.

Figure 272

167a Ovary 1-celled; seeds several to many. (Some species seemingly 2-celled by intrusion of placenta.) WATER-LEAF FAMILY....168

167b Ovary with more than one cell.............................169

168a Lobes of corolla fringed (a); calyx not much enlarged in fruit. Fig. 273..........................MIAMI MIST, *Phacelia purshii* Buckl.

Native annual; erect, much branched, pubescent, ½—1½ ft. high. Leaves 1—3 in. long, pinnately divided, the upper ones sessile. Flowers blue or white; 10—20 in., 1-sided racemes. Fruit a many seeded capsule, pedicels considerably elongated.

Often common in gardens, fields and waste places. April—June.

Other names: Pursh's Phacelia, Scorpion-weed.

Figure 273

168b Lobes of corolla entire, not fringed; calyx much enlarged in fruit. Fig. 274..........................*NYCTELEA, Ellisia nyctelea* L.

Native annual, with scattered long pubescence and forked stems up to a foot high. Leaves pinnately divided 2—4 in. long. Flowers solitary, opposite the leaves, the calyx greatly enlarging in fruit up to an inch or more across; corolla bell-shaped, pale lavender; fruit a globose capsule up to ¼ in. across, with 2 cells and 4 seeds.

In gardens, grainfields and moist wasteland. April—July.

Other names: Ellisia, Common Ellisia, Field Nyctelea.

Figure 274

169a A yellow, leafless, thread-like plant twining around other plants on which it lives parasitically. Dodder Family.............176

169b Not parasitic 170

170a Stamens and corolla lobes 5 (or more)....................171

170b Stamens and corolla lobes 4; leaves all arising from the ground; corolla dry and membraneous. Plantain Family...........195

171a Fruit with 2 or 4 nut-like seeds. Borage Family............148

171b Fruit a capsule or pod with few to many seeds............172

172a Twining (or trailing) vines, flowers usually showy. MORNING-GLORY FAMILY 173

172b Not twining; style simple, ending in a single terminal stigma. NIGHTSHADE FAMILY 177

173a Style divided into two elongate stigmas....................174

173b Style ending in a globose stigma (or stigmas)...............175

174a Flowers 1½ in. or more across; 2 large bracts at base of calyx. (a) Fig. 275.....WILD MORNING-GLORY, *Convolvulus sepium* L.

Figure 275

Native perennial with long persistent rootstocks, twining or trailing to a length of 10 ft. or more. Leaves, 2—5 in. long, triangular and hastate with slender petiole. Flowers solitary, from the leaf nodes, pink with white stripes or wholly white, about 2 in. long. Fruit a globular, thin-walled capsule, with 2 cells and 2—4 blackish seeds.

Widely distributed and a very annoying weed in cultivated fields. June—Aug.

Other names: Hedge Bindweed, Bracted Bindweed, Devil's-vine, Lily-bind, Rutland Beauty, Hedge-lily.

131

**174b Flowers 1 in. or less across, calyx without bracts. Fig. 276......
............................BINDWEED, Convolvulus arvensis L.**

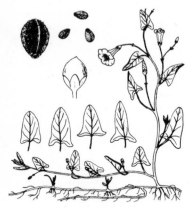

European perennial, s l e n d e r with creeping rhizomes and trailing stems 1—3 ft. long. Leaves 1—2 in. long, sagitate or hastate. Flowers 1—4 arising from the leaf nodes, white or pinkish. Fruit an ovate, thin-walled capsule with 2 cells and 2—4 dull grayish-brown seeds.

Widely distributed in fields and cultivated land. May—Aug.

Other names: Small-flowered Morning-glory, Creeping Jenny, Green-vine, Corn-lily, Lap-love, Hedge-bells.

Figure 276

**175a Leaves entire, heart-shaped; flowers 2—3 in. long. Fig. 277....
........................MORNING-GLORY, Ipomea purpurea (L.)**

Tropical annual, pubescent, sturdy stems twining or trailing, up to 10 ft. long. Leaves 2—4 in. wide, dark green. Flowers, 1—5 arising from the leaf nodes, blue, purple, pink, white or variegated. Fruit a thin-walled globular capsule, with usually 3 cells and 4—6 black seeds.

Escaped from cultivation as an ornamental to gardens, fields, and waste land. July— Oct.

Other name: Rope-wind.

Figure 277

175b Leaves three-lobed; flowers usually less than 2 in. long. Fig. 278
........IVY-LEAVED MORNING-GLORY, *Ipomea hederacea* (L.)

Tropical annual, pubescent climbing or trailing to a length of 2—6 ft. Leaves as pictured, 2—5 in. long. Flowers 1—3 from leaf nodes, light blue or purplish with white tube. Fruit a depressed-globular 3-celled capsule with 4—6 blackish seeds.

An escaped ornamental frequently found in gardens and fields. July—Oct.

Figure 278

DODDER FAMILY

176a Stigmas elongate, slender (a). Fig. 279. (Shown here parasiting clover.)..........CLOVER DODDER, *Cuscuta epithymum* Murr.

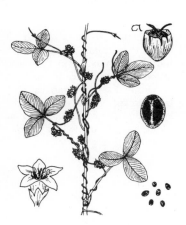

European annual with slender, red stems and sessile pinkish flowers about 1/12 in. long, in small dense clusters. Calyx and corolla with 4 or 5 lobes. Fruit a 2-celled, 4-seeded capsule opening by a lid and topped with the withered corolla.

Parasitic on clovers, alfalfa and other legumes and widely scattered. June—Sept.

Other name: Thyme Dodder. S M A L L-SEEDED ALFALFA DODDER, *C. planiflora* Tenore with white flowers 1/12 in. across and LARGE-SEEDED ALFALFA DODDER, *C. indecora* Choisy with white flowers 1/8 in. across and knobbed stigmas, both damage alfalfa as well as some other plants.

Figure 279

176b Stigmas ball-shaped (a); capsule indehiscent. Fig. 280. (Shown here growing on alfalfa.) ....
.... FIELD DODDER, *Cuscuta pentagona*, Engelm.

Native annual, stems slender, pale-yellow. Corolla with 5 lobes, but few nearly-sessile flowers to each cluster. Seeds yellow to reddish-brown.

Widely distributed, parasitic on many species of plants.

Other names: Love - v i n e , Large-seeded Dodder.

FLAX DODDER, *C. epilinum* Weihe w i t h reddish-yellow stems, yellowish-white flowers and slender stigmas, is a European introduced pest of flax.

Figure 280

NIGHTSHADE FAMILY

177a Fruit, a dry, spine-covered capsule (a); flower funnel-shaped. Fig. 281 .... JIMSON-WEED, *Datura stramonium* L.

Tropical annual, with thick green-to-purplish stems 1—5 ft. high. Leaves thin, irregularly lobed 2—8 in. long. Flowers white to violet 3—4 in. long and 1½—2 in. across. Fruit a 4-celled capsule 1½—2 in. high; seeds many, blackish, about ⅛ in. long.

Figure 281

177b Fruit a fleshy berry **178**

178a Anthers lightly connected at their sides and openings at the apical end; corolla star-shaped. Genus *Solanum*...................179

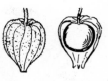

178b Anthers free from each other; fruiting calyx inflated into a bladder-like body enclosing the fruit. Fig. 282................182

Figure 282

179a Corolla white, about 1/3 in. across; fruit purplish-black. Fig. 283 ....BLACK NIGHTSHADE, *Solanum nigrum* L.

European annual, stems erect or spreading, o f t e n much branched, 1—2½ ft. high. Leaves 1—3 in. long, thin and often with two sides unequal. Flowers in umbels of 3—8; corolla white; anthers yellow, prominent. Berries when ripe, black, about 1/3 in. in diameter; seeds, numerous, disk-shaped, yellowish to brownish.

In gardens, fields, and waste places. July—Oct.

Other names: Poison-berry, Garden Nightshade, Hound's-berry, Deadly Nightshade.

Figure 283

179b Corolla purplish, yellow or white, more than ½ in. across; fruit red or yellow when ripe...................................180

180a Plants with prickles or thorns; fruit yellow when ripe........181

180b Plants without prickles or thorns; fruit red when ripe; corolla purple, violet or white. Fig. 284...............................
................CLIMBING NIGHTSHADE, *Solanum dulcamara* L.

Figure 284

Eurasian perennial, woody at base, climbing or trailing, 3—8 ft. long. Leaves entire or with 1 or 2 basal lobes, as pictured, 2—4 in. long and up to 2½ in. wide, dark green. Flowers several in cymose clusters; stamens yellow; corolla wheel-shaped, purple violet or occasionally white, about ½ in. across. Fruit a bright red, many seeded berry; seeds disk-shaped, light yellow.

In moist waste places. May —Sept.

O t h e r names: Bittersweet, Blue Bindweed, Woody Nightshade, Poison-berry, Scarlet-berry, Dogwood, Matrimony vine.

181a Fruit enclosed in a spiny calyx (a); flowers yellow. Fig. 285....
....................BUFFALO BURR, *Solanum rostratum* Dunal

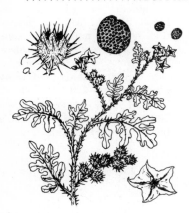

Figure 285

Native annual, densely covered w i t h star-shaped pubescence; stems erect, branched and heavily set with yellow prickles; 1— 2½ ft. high. Leaves with several deeply-cut lobes, as pictured, 2—5 in. long. Flowers yellow, about 1 in. across, somewhat irregular. Fruit a berry wholly enclosed within the calyx which in turn is covered with long prickles, having a diameter of an inch or more including the prickles. Seeds disk-shaped, about 1/10th in. across, brownish-black.

In barnlots, pastures and waste places, this was the original food plant of the Colorado Potato Beetle. May—Sept.

Other names: Sand Bur, Beaked Nightshade, Prickly Potato, Texas Thistle.

181b Fruit not enclosed by calyx and not prickly (a); flowers white or pale lavender. Fig. 286..HORSE NETTLE, *Solanum carolinense* **L.**

Native perennial, with fine stellate pubescence, erect, branched, stem covered with long yellow prickles 1—3 ft. high. Leaves pinnately lobed, 2—6 in. long. Flowers in cymose racemes; anthers y e l l o w, corolla wheel-or-star-shaped. Fruit yellow when ripe, about 2/3 in. in diameter; seeds disk-shaped, yellowish.

In pastures, cultivated fields and waste land.

Other names: Bull Nettle, Sandbrier, Wild Tomato, Apple-of-Sodom, Tread-Softly.

Figure 286

182a Corolla yellow or greenish-yellow; fruit a fleshy 2-celled berry.183

182b Corolla pale blue, a dry 3—5 celled berry. Fig. 287...........
....................APPLE-OF-PERU, *Nicandra physalodes* **(L.)**

South American annual, with angled stem, 2—5 ft. high. Leaves, pinnately lobed, 2—8 in. long, 1—4 in. wide. Flowers as broad as long (1—1½ in.), blue. Calyx, in fruit about 1—1½ in. in diameter, as pictured enclosing a ½ in. berry, which is dry when mature; seeds flattened, kidney-shaped, orange-brown.

In gardens, fields and wasteland July—Sept.

Figure 287

183a Plants thickly covered with a sticky pubescence, husk angled and sunken at its base..184

183b Plants glabrous or sparingly pubescent; husk ovoid with but little evidence of angles or being sunken at its base. Fig. 288......
........PRAIRIE GROUND-CHERRY, *Physalis lanceolata* **Michx.**

Native perennial, from a slender rootstalk; stem erect 1—2 ft. high. Leaves lanceolate or spatulate, usually entire, 1—3 in. long. Flowers dull-yellow with a brownish center, about 2/3 in. across. Fruit a greenish-yellow to yellow berry; seeds flattened.

In pastures, meadows and waste places. July—Sept.

Figure 288

184a Flowers less than ½ in. in diameter, anthers usually purplish; plant an annual with fibrous root system. Fig. 289.............
.........LOW HAIRY GROUND-CHERRY, *Physalis pubescens* **L.**

Native annual, much branched, villous-pubescent, 8—15 in. high. Leaves thin, 1—2½ in. long. Flowers about 1/3 in. across, yellow with dark center and anthers usually purplish. Husk sharply five angled, with sunken base and often pointed apex; berry yellow about ½ in. in diameter.

Widely distributed in sandy soil; sometimes cultivated for its fruit. July—Sept.

Other names: Strawberry-tomato, Husk-tomato, Dwarf Cape-gooseberry.

Figure 289

184b Flowers more than ½ in. across, anthers usually yellow; plant growing from a creeping rootstock. Fig. 290.................
......CLAMMY GROUND-CHERRY, *Physalis heterophylla*, Nees.

Figure 290

Native perennial, e r e c t though often reclining when mature, 2—3 ft. high, covered with a glandular viscid pubescence. Leaves thick 2—4 in. long. Flowers about ¾ in. across, greenish-yellow with darker center, and anthers usually yellow. Fruit a 2-celled yellow berry, with many flattened seeds, enclosed within a ribbed husk.

Widely spread on poor soils and in fields, pastures, etc. June—Aug.

Other name: Husk-tomato.

Several other similar species of native ground-cherries may be somewhat weedy.

185a Fertile stamens (with anthers) 2 or 4........................186

185b Fertile stamens 5. FIGWORT FAMILY......................188

186a Ovary with but one seed in each cell; ovary 4-lobed with thread-like style arising at intersection of dividing grooves; stems mostly square. MINT FAMILY...................................158

186b Ovary with more than 1 seed in each cell.................187

187a Ovary 1-celled; whitish, yellowish or purplish parasites securing nutriment from the roots of other plants. BROOMRAPE FAMILY 194

187b Ovary 2-celled; seeds numerous, filaments of stamens usually covered with hairs..188

FIGWORT FAMILY

188a Fertile stamens (with anthers) 2 or 4; leaves whorled, opposite or alternate 190

188b Fertile stamens 5; corolla rotate; leaves alternate...........189

189a Plant with a thick woolly covering; flowers yellow. Fig. 291....
.....................COMMON MULLEIN, *Verbascum thapsus* L.

Eurasian biennial, erect, usually simple, heavy stem 2—7 ft. high. Leaves thick and covered with a dense, branched pubescence, 2—12 in. long. Flowers yellow, 2/3—1 in. across; stamens unequal (3 short and 4 longer). Fruit a 2-celled, many-seeded globular capsule about ¼ in. in diameter; seeds dark brown.

In pastures, meadows and waste land; widely distributed and very common. June—Oct.

Other names: Candle-wick, Flannel-leaf, Torches, Velvetdock, Big-taper, Jacob's-staff, Blanket-leaf, Ice-leaf.

Figure 291

189b Plant wholly glabrous or nearly so; dark green; flowers pinkish or yellowish-white. Fig. 292...................................
.....................MOTH MULLEIN, *Verbascum blattaria* L.

Eurasian biennial, erect, slender 2—6 ft. high. Leaves 1—10 in. long, dark green. Flowers in loose terminal racemes 1—2 ft. long; corolla pinkish or yellowish white, 1 in. or less across. Fruit a 2-celled, globular capsule about 1/3 in. in diameter and bearing numerous dark-brown seeds.

Widely distributed in pastures, waste land, etc. June—Sept.

Figure 292

190a Corolla with a spur. (See Fig. 293a).......................191

190b Corolla without a spur...................................192

191a Plant erect; flowers yellow. Fig. 293.........................
......................BUTTER-AND-EGGS, *Linaria vulgaris* Hill

Eurasian perennial, growing in clumps from creeping roots, erect somewhat branched, 1—2½ ft. high. Leaves linear, sessile ½— 1½ in. wide. Flowers in dense terminal racemes, light yellow with orange spot on palate, 1— 1½ in. long. Fruit a 2-celled, many-seeded capsule; seeds disk-shaped, blackish.

In meadows, pastures and waste land. June—Oct.

Other names: Yellow Toad-flax, Ramstead, Rabbit-flower, W i l d Snapdragon.

Figure 293

191b Plant trailing; leaves with 3—5 palmate veins. Fig. 294........
...............KENILWORTH IVY, *Cymbalaria muralis*, Gaertn.

Eurasian annual, glabrous, trailing stem 1 ft. or longer. Leaves, as pictured, 3—5 lobed and veined, up to 1 in. across. Flowers, solitary in the axils, blue or lilac, about 1/3 in. long. Fruit a 2-celled, thin-walled, capsule bearing many brownish-black seeds.

In lawns, gardens, and waste land; escaped from cultivation as an ornamental. June—Sept.

Other names: Coliseum Ivy, Wandering Jew, Mother-of-Thousands, Aaron's-Beard, Pennywort.

Figure 294

192a Stamens 2 193

192b Anther bearing stamens 4. Fig. 295..........................
............**MARYLAND FIGWORT,** *Scrophularia marilandica* **L.**

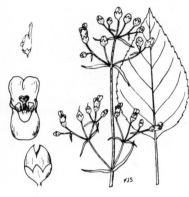

Native perennial, nearly glabrous, erect 4-angled stems, 3—10 ft. high. Leaves thin 3—12 in. long. Flowers greenish-purple, about 1/3 in. long; sterile stamen deep purple.

In waste land, road sides, etc. July—Sept.

Other names: Pilewort, Heal-all, Carpenter's-Square.

HARE FIGWORT, *S. lanceolata*, Pursh is a highly similar plant but the sterile stamen is yellowish-green, and the outside of the corolla shining instead of dull.

Figure 295

193a Leaves almost wholly glabrous, entire or with but small teeth. Flowers white. Fig. 296...................................
.................**PURSLANE SPEEDWELL,** *Veronica peregrina* **L.**

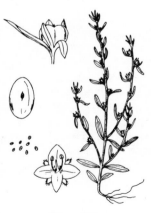

Native annual (often a winter annual), erect, usually branched, 3—12 in. high. Leaves linear or spatulate, sometimes with a few obscure teeth, ½—1 in. long. Flowers white, about 1/10 in. across. Fruit a heart-shaped capsule about ⅛ in. high with many shining, deep yellow seeds.

Common in gardens and fields. April—Oct.

Other names: Neckweed, Winter Purslane.

Figure 296

193b Leaves hairy, with coarse teeth; flowers blue. Fig. 297........
...................CORN SPEEDWELL, Veronica arvensis L.

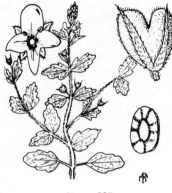

Figure 297

Eurasian annual (or winter annual) pubescent, erect or spreading and branched 3—10 in. high. Leaves up to ½ in. long. Flowers blue (sometimes nearly white) about 1/10 in. across. Fruit a heart-shaped, capsule about 1/10 in. across with numerous yellow seeds.

In dry pastures, lawns and waste land; widely distributed. March—Sept.

Other names: Wall Speedwell, Rock Speedwell.

Several other species of this genus which are similar in size and general appearance to the two species pictured here occur in our area and may sometimes be weedy.

194a Calyx 4-toothed (if split see second species); stems usually branched. Fig. 298........BROOM-RAPE, Orobanche ramosa L.

Figure 298

European annual with slender, usually branched stems 3—15 in. high. Scales (vestigial leaves) scattered along stem, as pictured, about ¼ in. long. Flowers rather numerous in open, terminal spikes; calyx 4-toothed; corolla 2-lipped, ½—¾ in. long. Fruit, a many-seeded capsule; seeds fine, yellowish brown.

Parasites the roots of hemp, tobacco and sometimes tomato. June—Aug.

Other names: Branched Broom-rape, Strangle-tare.

CLOVER BROOM-RAPE O. minor J. E. Smith parasitizing the roots of clover, and growing 3—20 in. high is unbranched and has its calyx definitely split into 2 parts of 2 lobes each. It came from Europe and is also known as Hell-root or Devil's-root.

143

194b Calyx 5-toothed, stem unbranched. Fig. 299.................
........LOUISIANA BROOMRAPE, *Orobanche ludoviciana* Nutt

Native annual, with thick sticky stems, sometimes growing in clusters, ½—1 ft. high. Flower ½—2/3 in. long; calyx with five acute lobes and 1—2 bracts at the base; corolla 2-lipped, purplish; anthers woolly.

Grows as a parasite on the roots of tobacco and several other plants. Rather widely distributed especially in the Central States.

Other name: Strangle-tare.

Figure 299

PLANTAIN FAMILY

195a Leaf blades fully half as wide as long. Fig. 300.
(a) COMMON PLANTAIN, *Plantago major* L.
(b) RUGEL'S PLANTAIN, *P. rugelii* Dcne.

These two species often grow together and pass with most folks as the same plant.

Both are perennials; *major* is of European origin while the other is native. They arise from a short, heavy rootstock. Leaves 2—10 in. long, often lying rather flat to the ground; sometimes standing more erect. Flowers in long cylindrical spikes, occasional ones nearly 3 ft. in length; sepals, petals, and stamens 4 each. Fruit a 2-celled, 2-seeded capsule opening by a lid, as pictured (pyxis).

Figure 300

Distinguishing characters are: *Rugell's Plantain:* lid of capsule much taller than the cup (b), 4 to 9 seeds; fruiting spike long and thin, rather open: leaf blades thinner and brighter green, the petioles rather slender and crimson or purple at their base. *Common Plantain:* lid of capsule about equal in height with the cup (a), 5 to 16 seeds: spike usually very dense; leaf blades rather thick and duller green, the petioles longer, usually green at the base.

195b **Leaf blades narrow, much less than ½ as wide as long.....196**

196a **Leaves linear** 197

196b **Leaves lanceolate. Fig. 301**.................................
................**BUCKHORN PLANTAIN,** *Plantago lanceolata* **L.**

Eurasian perennial (sometimes biennial), somewhat pubescent, with tufts of brown hairs at base of leaves. Leaves 3—5 ribbed, 3—10 in. long and up to 1 in. wide. Flowering spike at first short and thick but lengthening in fruit to a possible 3 in. or more and up to 2 ft. or more in height. Capsule 2-seeded; seeds glossy, light to dark brown.

Widespread and too common in lawns, meadows, and waste land. June—Sept.

Other names: English Plantain, Narrow-leaved Plantain, Rib-grass, Ripple Plantain, Snake Plantain, Dog's-ribs, Cat's-cradles, Rat-tail, Henplant.

Figure 301

197a **Bracts much longer than the flowers; plants dark green. Fig. 302**
................**BRACTED PLANTAIN,** *Plantago aristata* **Michx.**

Native annual (or winter annual) with fruiting scapes up to 18 in. tall. Leaves 3-ribbed and up to 5 in. long and ½ in. wide. Flowers whitish, sometimes maturing seeds without opening. Fruit a pyxis (opening by a lid) and containing 2 seeds, as pictured.

In pastures, meadows, and waste land. May—Oct.

Other names: Rat-Tail Plantain, Clover Choker, Western Buckhorn, Western Ripple-grass.

Figure 302

145

197b Bracts no longer than the flowers; pale green, silky or woolly. Fig. 303.........PURSH'S PLANTAIN, *Plantago purshii* R. & S.

Native annual, woolly, with fruiting stems up to 15 in. high. Leaves linear, 1—3 veined. Flowers whitish, often cleistogamous. Capsules opening transversely at about the middle and containing 2 light brown seeds.

In dry pastures, meadows, and waste land. May—Aug.

Other name: Salt-and-pepper-plant.

Still other similar species of Plantains may at times seem to belong with the weeds.

Figure 303

MADDER FAMILY

203a Leaves in whorls...204

203b Leaves opposite. Fig. 305.....................................
.................ROUGH BUTTON-WEED, *Diodia teres* Walt.

Native annual, much branched, ascending or prostrate, stems up to 2½ ft. long. Leaves very rough, linear or somewhat so, ½—1½ in. long. Flowers whitish, lilac or purple, about ¼ in. long. Fruit top-shaped, covered with a sticky pubescence, grayish brown.

In cultivated fields and waste land especially where dry. Common in the South and sometimes invading northern areas. July—Sept.

Other names: Poverty-weed, Poor Joe, Poor-land-weed.

Figure 305

204a Fruit covered with short hooked bristles, annual. Fig. 306......
...............................CLEAVERS, *Galium aparine* L.

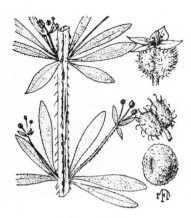

Annual (a native of Europe and possibly also of our country) with limber scrambling, 4-angled stems, thickly set with backward pointing bristles, up to 4 or 5 ft. long. Leaves 1—2 in. long in whorls of 6—8. Flowers in few flowered cymes, white. Fruit about ⅛ in. across.

Common in thickets, fence rows and waste land, widely distributed. May—Aug.

Other names: B e d s t r a w , Goose-grass, C a t c h - w e e d , Sweethearts, G r i p - g r a s s , Scratch-grass.

Figure 306

**204b Fruit smooth; perennial; leaves in whorls of 5 or 6. Fig. 307.....
......ROUGH BEDSTRAW,** *Galium triflorum asprelliforme* **Fern.**

Native perennial with much branched, scrambling stems up to 6 ft. long. Leaves narrowly oval to oblanceolate, 1/3—2/3 in. long. Flowers white, in several- to many-flowered cymes. Fruit smooth, about 1/10 in. across.

In moist fields and waste ground. July—Sept.

Other name: Kidney-vine.

Several other species of this genus may act as weeds, one *G. verum* L. has yellow flowers, but all others are white.

Figure 307

205a Woody shrub; flowers 1/6 in. long, campanulate, fruit red. Fig. 308.........BUCK-BRUSH, *Symphoricarpos orbiculatus* **Moench.**

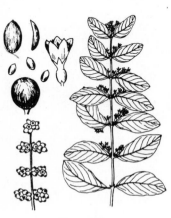

Native perennial shrub, often much branched 2—5 ft. high. Leaves opposite 1—2 in. long. Flowers in dense axillary clusters, pinkish 1/6 in. long. Fruit a purplish red 2-seeded berry 1/6 in. or less in diameter, persisting through the winter.

Often common in pastures and fields. July. Two other species with white berries sometimes escape from cultivation.

Other names: Coral-berry, Turkey-berry, Indian-currant.

Figure 308

205b Woody vine; flowers 1 in. long, two lipped; fruit black. Fig. 309 . . . . JAPANESE HONEYSUCKLE, *Lonicera japonica* Thunb.

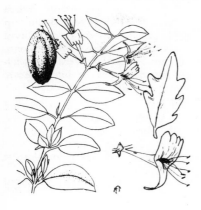

Asiatic woody vine with slender, hairy, trailing or twining stems of considerable length. Leaves, opposite, dark green 1—3 in. long. Flowers paired from upper axils, pinkish or white, later becoming yellow. Fruit a pair of black berries about 1/3 in. in diameter.

Common throughout much of our Southeast in thickets, fields, and waste land; escaped from cultivation.

Other name: Chinese Honeysuckle.

Figure 309

206a Flowering heads elongated, with their many bracts tipped with a sharp bristle. Fig. 310 . . . . . . TEASEL, *Dipsacus sylvestris* Huds.

European biennial, the thick stem covered with short downturned prickles 3—6 ft. high. Leaves opposite, sessile, up to 1 ft. long. Flowering heads elongating in fruit to 3 or 4 in.; flowers lilac 1/3—½ in. long. Fruit a 4-angled achene about 1/6 in. long.

Along roadsides, and in fields and waste land. It was once used in carding wool. July—Sept.

Other names: Card Teasel, Venus-cup, Prickly-back, Adam's-flannel, Church-brooms, Gipsy-combs, Indian-thistle.

Figure 310

206b Flowering heads flattened, bracts without prickles. Fig. 311....
........................FIELD SCABIOSUS, *Scabiosa arvensis* L.

European perennial, pubescent, sparingly branched, 1—3 ft. high. Leaves, 3—8 in. long, entire or deeply cut into narrow lobes. Flowers purplish-lilac about ½ in. long, numerous in flattened heads. Fruit an achene about 1/6 in. long.

In waste land, meadows, etc. A closely related species S. *atropurpurea* L. with flowers of many colors is a well-known ornamental.

O t h e r names: Pincushion, Gypsy-rose, Blue-caps.

Figure 311

207a Fruit 1-seeded, indehiscent. Fig. 312.........................
........................STAR CUCUMBER, *Sicyos angulatus* L.

Native annual climbing vine with angled stems. Sometimes 20 ft. or more long. Leaves, as pictured, 3—8 in. across. Flowers staminate in a long stemmed raceme, with three stamens; pistilate several sessile flowers in a head at the end of a long peduncle. Fruit in clusters of 3—10, yellowish and covered with rough spines. The single seed ovate, flattened, black, about ½ in. long.

Widespread east of the Mississippi in thickets and waste land. June—Sept.

Figure 312

Other names: One-seeded Bur Cucumber, Nimble Kate.

207b Fruit 4-seeded, dehiscent. Fig. 313............................
................BALSAM APPLE, *Echinocystis lobata* Michx.

Native annual with tendril-climbing stems 15—25 ft. long. Leaves deeply, 3—7 lobed. Flowers: staminate many in a compound raceme; pistillate usually solitary. Fruit, about 2 in. long, ovoid, green, covered with prickles, 2-celled, the 4 flattened brown seeds about ¾ in. long.

In fence rows and waste land, especially on low rich ground. Sometimes used as a trellis ornamental. Aug.—Sept.

Other names: Wild Cucumber, Mock Apple, Creeping Jenny.

Figure 313

208a Leaves broadly ovate and clasping the stem. Fig. 314..........
..........VENUS'S LOOKING-GLASS, *Specularia perfoliata* (L.)

Native annual with slender, weak, angled stem, ½—2 ft. long. Leaves as pictured, ¼—1 in. wide. Flowers blue, wheel-shaped, in the leaf axils, usually solitary, ½—¾ in. across. Fruit a capsule with many dark brown, lens-shaped seeds.

In dry fields and pastures. June—Aug.

Other name: Clasping Bellwort.

Figure 314

208b Leaves ovate to lanceolate, 3—6 in. long. Fig. 315.............
.................TALL BELLFLOWER, *Campanula americana* **L.**

Native annual or biennial, e r e c t , sometimes sparingly branched, 2—6 ft. high. Leaves thin, 3—6 in. long. Flowers blue (sometimes quite pale) about 1 in. across, in long terminal, leafy spikes. Fruit a many-seeded capsule.

In fence rows and thickets. July—Sept.

Figure 315

209a Corolla nearly 1 in. long. Fig. 316...........................
......................GREAT LOBELIA, *Lobelia siphilitica* **L.**

Native perennial, stem heavy, erect or declining, 1—3 ft. high. Leaves 2—6 in. long and up to 2 in. wide. Flowers bright blue (rarely white or nearly so), 4/5—1 in. long, in leafy, terminal spikes. Fruit a 2-celled, many-seeded capsule.

Rather widely distributed, in damp soil of pastures and fields. July—Oct.

Other name: Blue cardinalflower.

Figure 316

209b Flowers ¼ in. long, or less. Fig. 317.........................
...........................INDIAN TOBACCO, *Lobelia inflata* L.

Native annual, (or winter annual), stem branching, 1—3 ft. high. Leaves thin, 1—2½ in. long. Flowers pale blue, scattered in racemes; capsule inflated with vertical ribs and transverse veining. Capsule 2-celled, with many yellow brown seeds.

Widely distributed in dry fields and thickets. It is used in medicine and is poisonous. July—Nov.

Other names: Eyebright, Asthma-weed, Bladder-pod, Puke-weed, Gagroot, Emetic-weed.

Figure 317

COMPOSITE FAMILY

1a All of the individual flowers composing the head, strap-shaped (ligulate) ray flowers; juice milky. Fig. 318.............................2

Figure 318

1b At least part of the flowers in the head tubular (those on the margin of the head may or may not be strap-shaped); juice not milky. Fig. 319. 14

Figure 319

2a (a, b, c, d) Pappus a ring of short, blunt scales (a); flowers blue (occasionally white). Fig. 320 .... CHICORY, *Cichorium intybus* **L.**

European perennial, stems stiff, somewhat ridged and branched, from thickened root, 1—3 ft. high. Leaves irregularly lobed or upper ones sometimes entire; many of them clasping, 1—6 in. long. Flowering heads 1—1½ in. across, rather numerous; flowers usually bright blue. Achenes light brown, about ⅛ in. long.

Often common in waste land, along roadsides, and in fields. Introduced as a substitute (the roots) for coffee. July—Oct.

Other name: Succory.

Figure 320

2b Pappus of plume-like bristles (a). Fig. 321 3

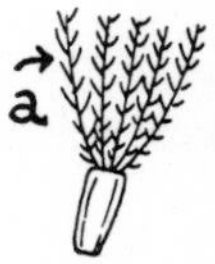

Figure 321

2c Pappus of simple unbranched bristles (though often serrate). Fig. 322 6

Figure 322

2d Pappus none, flowers yellow. Fig. 323........................
.......................NIPPLEWORT, *Lapsana communis* L.

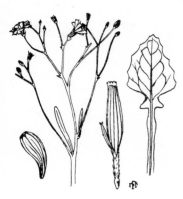

Figure 323

European annual. Stems slender freely branched 1—3 ft high; leaves alternate, glabrous, up to 4 in. long. Heads many, about ¼ in. across in an open panicle; flowers 8—12 all ligulate, yellow; achenes about 1/6 in. long, spindle shaped, gray.

Locally introduced on both coasts and sometimes abundant in fields, waste land, etc. June—Sept.

Other names: Dock Cress, Succory, Bullogan.

3a All of the leaves growing from the thickened rootstock........4

3b Plants with erect, leaf-bearing stems.........................5

4a Achenes with long, slender beak. Fig. 324.....................
.............LONG-ROOTED CAT'S-EAR, *Hypochaeris radicata* L.

Figure 324

European perennial; stems glabrous, often branched, with scattered short bracts, 1—2 ft. high. Leaves all basal, irregularly dentate, 2—6 in. long. Heads 1 in. or more across; flowers longer than the involucre, yellow; receptacle with soft pointed chaffy bracts; achenes roughened, with beak as long or longer than the body and barbed, reddish brown.

In meadows, lawns, and waste land. May—Sept.

Other names: Gosmore, Coast Dandelion, False Dandelion, Flatweed.

4b Achenes not beaked (a). Fig. 325..............................
.....................**FALL DANDELION,** *Leontodon autumnalis* **L.**

Figure 325

European perennial with slender, often-branched scape ½—2 ft. high. Leaves all basal, narrow, pinnately toothed, 3—8 in. long. Heads about 1 in. across with many bright yellow flowers. Achenes brown, 5 ribbed and about 1/6 in. long.

Along roadsides and in pastures and waste land. June—Oct.

Other names: Hawkbit, Lion's-tooth, Dog-dandelion, Arnica.

5a Plant glabrous. Fig. 326.....................................
..............**YELLOW GOAT'S-BEARD,** *Tragopogon pratensis* **L.**

Figure 326

European biennial, stem branching from thickened fleshy tap root 1—3 ft. high. Leaves, alternate, accuminate, clasping at base, up to 10 in. long. Heads 1—2½ in. across with about 8 bracts in the involucre, rays numerous, light yellow. Achenes, except in outer row, beaked, 5 angled, about 1/3 in. long.

Along roadsides and in fields and waste land. June—Sept.

Other names: Morning-sun, Meadow S a l s i f y , Noon-flower, Star-of-Jeru-salem.

VEGETABLE-OYSTER, *T. porrifolius* L., with involucral bracts longer than the rays and with purple flowers, escapes from gardens where it is raised for its edible roots.

5b Plant covered with a sticky pubescence. Fig. 327 . . . .
. . . . **OX-TONGUE,** *Picris hieracioides* **L.**

Figure 327

European annual or biennial, branched, 1—3 ft. high. Leaves, basal, petioled, those of stem sessile, 1—6 in. long. Heads many, ½—1 in. across; rays, 5-toothed, yellow. Achenes about ⅛ in. long with a short beak; Pappus white or nearly so.

In waste land and fields. June—Sept.

Other names: Bugloss, Hawkweed Picris.

P. echioides L., a similar weed, distinguished by its broad outer involucral bracts, has similar habitats.

6a Leaves all basal, (occasionally 1 or 2 leaves and short bracts on the scape). 7
6b Plants with leafy stems 9
7a Flowering scapes branched to bear several heads 8
7b Flowering scapes bearing but one head. Fig. 328 . . . .
. . . .**COMMON DANDELION,** *Taraxacum officinale* **Weber**

Figure 328

Perennial, apparently introduced from Europe although some contend it is native to our country, arising from long, thick, yellow roots; flowering scapes hollow, up to 1½ ft. high. Leaves variable but usually deeply lobed, 3—12 in. long. Heads 1—2 in. across and containing up to 200 or more golden yellow flowers, the outer bracts of the i n v o l u c r e strongly reflexed; achenes greenish-brown.

Widely distributed and often very abundant in lawns, fields, and waste ground. Jan.—Dec.

Other names: Blow-ball, Lion's-tooth, Irish Daisy.

RED-SEEDED DANDELION, *T. erythrospermum* Andrz. averaging somewhat smaller than the above and easily distinguished by its dark red achenes, is often found growing with its sister species.

8a Flowers orange. Fig. 329.....................................
...............ORANGE HAWKWEED, *Hieracium aurantiacum* L.

European perennial, with long glandular hairs, scape 6—20 in. high. Leaves hirsute, 2—5 in. long. Heads up to 1 in. across, flowers orange or red. Achenes cylindrical, truncate, blackish.

In waste places, lawns and pastures. June—Aug.

Other names: Orange Paintbrush, Red Daisy, Missionary-weed.

Figure 329

8b Flowers yellow, leaves hirsute on both sides. Fig. 330..........
..............YELLOW PAINTBRUSH. *Hieracium pratense* Tausch

European perennial, c o v e r e d with long hairs, scapes up to 2 ft. high. Leaves light green, 2—5 in. long. Heads several or more, about ¾ in. across; flowers yellow.

In meadows, lawns, and pastures. June—Aug.

Other names: Devil's Paintbrush, Yellow-devil, F i e l d Hawkweed, King Devil.

Several other species of the genus are sometimes weedy.

Figure 330

9a Leaves linear, stiff; heads few-flowered, pink or purplish. Fig. 331.
........................RUSH PINK, *Lygodesmia juncea* (Pursh)

Native perennial with thick, woody root; ½—1½ ft. high. Leaves ½—2 in. long. Heads usually with only 5 flowers, solitary at end of branches ½—2/3 in. across; ligule of flower prominently notched at end, pink or rose-purple; pappus light brown.

This plains plant is often common in dry fields and along roadsides. June—Aug.

Other names: Skeleton-weed, Rush-like Lygodesmia, Wild Asparagus, Devil's Shoestring.

Figure 331

9b Leaves broader; flowers yellow or blue........................10

10a Flowers yellow 11

10b Flowers blue. Fig. 332.....................................
.....................BLUE LETTUCE, *Lactuca pulchella* (Pursh)

Native perennial, erect, glabrous, in part glaucous, 1—3 ft. high. Leaves 2—8 in. long, variable, those of the stem usually clasping. Heads ½—¾ in. across, fairly numerous in a paniculate corymb; rays bright blue or violet; pappus white; achenes brown, almost ¼ in. long, with short beak.

In pastures and waste land. July—Sept.

Other names: M i l k w e e d, Showy Lettuce.

Most of the members of this genus have yellow flowers, but two or three other species with

Figure 332

blue flowers, all of them annuals, may seem to be weeds.

11a Achene beaked or with a narrow neck at top. Fig. 333.........
.........................PRICKLY LETTUCE, *Lactuca scariola* L.

European annual (or winter annual), stems stiff, leafy, 2—7 ft. high. Leaves with prickly margins, often clasping at base, up to 10 in. long. Heads about 1/3 in. across, with 8—12 pale yellow flowers. Achenes about ⅛ in. long; pappus white.

In gardens, fields, and waste land. Aug.—Oct.

Other names: Compass-plant, Horse Thistle.

Figure 333

WILD LETTUCE, *L. canadensis* L. (Fig. 334), a native, glabrous annual or biennial and lacking the spines on the leaves, often grows with the above and in many ways is similar to it.

Figure 334

11b Achenes truncate above (ending abruptly), (see Fig. 335a); flowers 50 or more in each head...................................12
12a Heads 1 in. or more across; perennial spreading by rootstocks. Fig. 335..............FIELD SOW-THISTLE, *Sonchus arvensis* L.

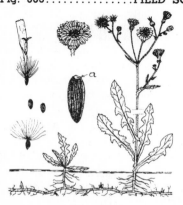

Eurasian perennial, erect, often branched, frequently glaucous, 2—4 ft. high. Leaves clasping, prickly dentate, 3—12 in. long. Heads about 1½ in. across, numerous and very showy; flowers brilliant yellow. Achenes about ⅛ in. long, reddish brown.

Along roadsides, in fields, and waste land. June—Sept.

Other names: Creeping Sow-Thistle, Perennial Sow-Thistle, Swine-Thistle

Figure 335

12b Heads smaller, less than 1 in. across 13

13a Leaf-auricles rounded (a); achenes longitudinally ribbed (b). Fig.
336 . . . . SPINY-LEAVED SOW-THISTLE, *Sonchus asper.* (L.)

European annual, erect from a tap root, up to 5 ft. high. Leaves heavily spined along edges but scarcely divided or lobed, 3—8 in. long. Heads ½ to about 1 in. across; flowers pale yellow. Achenes as pictured, orange brown.

In gardens, fields, and waste land. July—Sept.

Other name: Sharp-fringed Sow-thistle.

Figure 336

13b Leaf auricles acute (a); achenes wrinkled cross-wise (b). Fig. 337
. . . . COMMON SOW-THISTLE, *Sonchus oleraceus* L.

European annual, growing from a tap root, erect with branches, 1—8 ft. high. Leaved, lower ones with petioles, the upper leaves clasping, as pictured. Heads, ½ to about 1 in. across, fairly numerous; flowers pale yellow. Achenes, as pictured, brown.

Widely distributed on cultivated land. May—Oct.

Other names: Annual Sow-thistle, Hares-lettuce, Milk Tassel, Milk-thistle.

Figure 337

14a Anthers separate or merely touching but not grown together; flowers all tubular 15

14b Anthers attached to each other forming a hollow cylinder surrounding the style 22

15a Staminate and pistillate flowers in the same heads. Genus *Iva* . . 16

15b Staminate and pistillate flowers in different heads; involucre of pistillate flowers forming a closed woody body, roughed or covered with spines in fruit. Fig. 338 17

Figure 338

16a Each head arising from the axil of the narrow, entire leaves. Fig. 339 . . . . POVERTY WEED, *Iva axillaris* Pursh

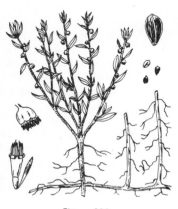

Figure 339

Native perennial, sometimes branched, glabrous or pubescent, 1—2 ft. high. Leaves with 3 veins, ½—1½ in. long. Heads about ¼ in. across, usually solitary in the leaf axils. Pistillate flowers 4 or 5, with tubular corolla. Achenes, lens-shaped, gray-brown, about 1/6 in. long.

In grain fields and waste land; growing from creeping roots. July —Sept.

Other names: Small-flowered Marsh Elder, Death Weed, Devil's Weed.

16b Heads arising from bare stems; leaves broad with coarse dentations. Fig. 340 . . . . BURWEED MARSH ELDER, *Iva xanthifolia* Nutt.

Figure 340

Native annual much branched, growing vigorously to a height of 3—10 ft. Leaves paler and canescent beneath, 3—10 in. long. Head, with about 5 pistillate and 10—15 staminate flowers in panicled spikes. Achenes about 1/6 in. long, with longitudinal ribs, blackish.

In fields, roadsides, and waste land; mostly of northern range, except in the West, where it ranges entirely down to Mexico. July—Sept.

Other names: False Ragweed, False Sunflower, Red-river-weed, Highwater-shrub.

17a The bracts of the involucre grown together to form a cup which surrounds the flowers.....................................19

17b Bracts of the involucre of the staminate heads separate, leaf-like; the pistillate heads forming a bur. See Fig. 342a..............18

18a With a 3-pronged yellow spine arising from the axil of each leaf, as pictured (a). Fig. 341......................................
.....................SPINY COCKLEBUR, *Xanthium spinosum* L.

Tropical annual, whitish pubescent, much branched, 1—3 ft. high. Leaves narrow with pinnate lobes (upper ones often entire), white-canescent beneath with spines in axil. Burs, as pictured, 1/3—½ in. long, pubescent, each containing 2 achenes.

Rather general throughout eastern U. S. in pastures, waste land, especially along streams. Aug.—Sept.

Other names: Spiny Clotbur, Spanish Thistle, Dagger-cocklebur, Burweed.

Figure 341

18b Leaves broad; without spines. Fig. 342.........................
............................COCKLEBUR, *Xanthium orientale* L.

Tropical annual, rough, much branched, 1—5 ft. high. Leaves long petioled, toothed or lobed and roughly pubescent. Burs as pictured, light brown, about ¾ in. long. Achenes 2 in. each bur, flattened.

Widely scattered and common in cultivated fields, waste land, and low places. Aug.—Oct.

Other names: Clotbur, Sheep-bur, Ditch-bur, Button-bur.

Figure 342

19a "Seed" (pistillate involucre) with but one circle of tubercles or prickles 20

19b "Seed" with scattered prickles, as pictured (a); leaves white with hairs. Fig. 343...
.........SILVER-LEAF POVERTY-WEED, *Franseria discolor* Nutt.

Native perennial, erect or ascending to 1 ft. high. Leaves green above, covered with dense white pubescence beneath, 2—5 in. long. Staminate heads in naked racemes 1—2 in. long; pistillate heads axillary, and having sharp, curved spines, light brown.

In meadows and fields, mostly western. July—Sept.

Other names: Bur-ragweed, White-weed.

Figure 343

20a Leaves pinnately parted or lobed. See Fig. 344a..............21

20b Leaves cut into 3—5 lobes (upper ones sometimes entire). Fig. 344.....................GREAT RAGWEED, *Ambrosia trifida* L.

Native annual, branched and vigorous growing to a height of 3—18 ft. Leaves usually 3—5 lobed and sometimes up to 1 ft. wide. Staminate heads up to 10 in. long and producing pale yellow pollen in great profusion. Pistillate heads clustered in the axils of upper leaves, brown and gray.

Common and widely distributed in rich land. July—Sept.

Other names: Horse-weed, Giant Ragweed, Crown-weed, Tall ambrosia, Buffalo-weed.

Figure 344

21a Leaves with simple pinnate lobes, as pictured (a), perennial. Fig. 345............**WESTERN RAGWEED,** *Ambrosia psilostachya* **DC.**

Native perennial, much branched, hispid, 2—6 ft. high. Leaves 2—5 in. long, usually but once pinnatifid, rough. Pistillate heads usually solitary; staminate heads in 2—6 in. racemes.

Widely distributed through the Mississippi Valley and westward.

Other name: Perennial Ragweed.

Figure 345

21b Leaves usually 2 or more times cut and divided; annual. Fig. 346
..................**HAY-FEVER WEED,** *Ambrosia artemisiifolia* **L.**

Native annual, much branched and roughly pubescent, 1—6 ft. high. Leaves variable but usually finely cut, 2—4 in. long. Staminate heads with 5—20 flowers produced in great abundance in many racemes 1—6 in. long; pistillate heads borne in groups of 2—3 in the axils of the leaves, the involucre inclosing the single flower and becoming woody, to house the one achene.

Widely distributed and very common in pastures, fields, etc. Aug.—Oct.

Figure 346

Other names: Ragweed, Blackweed, Hog-weed, Mayweed, Wild-tansy, Roman Wormwood, Carrott-weed.

22a No ray-flowers; all of the flowers of the head with tubular corollas (disk flowers) only...**23**

22b Both tube-flowers (disk-flowers) and ray-flowers present. (*Grindelia* and several species of *Bidens* are occasionally rayless.).......**44**

23a Leaves (at least the lower ones) mainly opposite or whorled. Fig. 347.......**24**

Figure 347

23b Leaves alternate. Fig. 348.................**27**

Figure 348

24a Pappus 2—6 rigid awns (a); flowers usually deep yellow or orange. Fig. 349...........
.... SPANISH NEEDLES, page 194

Figure 349

24b Pappus of many fine bristles (a); flowers white, pink, lilac, red or purple; heads ¼ in. broad or less. THOROUGHWORTS.......**25**

25a Leafblades connate-perfoliate; flowers white. Fig. 350...........
........................BONESET, *Eupatorium perfoliatum* L.

Figure 350

Native perennial, pubescent, with heavy, moderately branched stems, 2—5 ft. high. Leaves opposite and united to surround the stem (occasionally in 3's), 4—8 in. long and up to 1½ in. wide. Heads about ¼ in. high with 10—20 white flowers (rarely blue). Achenes 5 angled, linear, about 1/10 in. long, black with yellow dots.

In pastures and waste ground, especially where damp. Aug.—**Sept.**

Other names: Ague-weed, Fever-weed, Sweating-plant, Common Thoroughwort.

25b Leaves with petioles..**26**

26a Flowers white, leaves opposite. Fig. 351.......................
..............WHITE SNAKEROOT, *Eupatorium rugosum* Houtt.

Native perennial, w i t h rather slender, much-branched stems 1—4 ft. high. Leaves thin, sharp pointed, 3—6 in. long and 1—3 in. wide. Heads 10—30 flowered, in dense corymbs; flowers brilliant white.

Common in woods, pastures, fields, and roadsides. Sometimes cultivated as an ornamental. Poisonous to cattle. Aug.—Sept.

Other names: Deerwort, Squaw-weed, Stevia, White Sanicle, Richweed.

Figure 351

26b Flowers pink to purple; leaves in whorls of 3 to 6. Fig. 352......
......................JOE-PYE-WEED, *Eupatorium dubium* Willd.

Native perennial, glabrous or sparingly pubescent, stems green or purple, 3—10 ft. high. Leaves in whorls, 3—12 in. long and up to 3 in. wide. Heads many, elongate with pinkish bracts and variably colored, pink to purple flowers.

Widely distributed and common, preferring damp locations. Aug.—Sept.

Other names: Trumpet-weed, Tall Boneset, Purple Boneset, Skunk-weed, Kidney-root.

Figure 352

27a (b, c) Leaves spiny (a); pappus plumose (b). Fig. 353. PLUMED THISTLES......41

Figure 353

27b Leaves spiny; pappus not plumose. PLUMELESS THISTLES....43

27c Leaves not spiny, pappus none, or if present not plumose......28

28a (b, c) Flowers yellow or greenish............................29

28b Flowers white or cream colored............................33

28c Flowers purplish, blue, red, or pink (yellow in Barnaby's Thistle).37

29a (b, c) Pappus none or a short crown, (see Fig. 355a); foliage strongly scented, stem solid......................................30

29b Pappus bristly; involucre bracts of heads tipped with yellowish spines (see Fig. 367). BARNABY'S THISTLE...................39a

29c Pappus of numerous fine, white bristles; bracts without spines; foliage not strong-scented; stem hollow. Fig. 354.................
....................COMMON GROUNDSEL, *Senecio vulgaris* L.

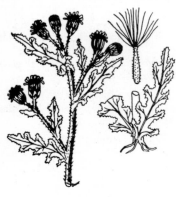

European annual or winter annual, erect or decumbent, often branched 5—15 in. high. Leaves pinnately lobed, 2—6 in. long. Heads about ¼ in. broad and ½ in. high in corymbs; outer involucral bracts with black tips; flowers many, yellow. Achenes about 1/6 in. long, brown with white pappus.

In waste places and cultivated fields.

Other n a m e s : Chickenweed, Simson, Bird-seed, Ragwort.

Figure 354

30a Heads ¼ to ½ in. broad, in a common corymb; pappus a short crown (a). Fig. 355 . . . . TANSY, *Tanacetum vulgare* L.

European perennial, stem stout, usually glabrous 1—3 ft. high. Leaves finely cut, as pictured, up to 1 ft. long. Heads numerous in dense clusters; flowers yellow; achenes yellow-brown with a short 5-toothed crown.

In waste places and roadsides, where it has escaped from gardens. July—Sept.

O t h e r names: Bitter-buttons, Ginger-plant, Parsley-fern, Hind-head.

Figure 355

30b Heads 1/6 in. or less broad, in a pannicle; pappus none 31

31a A woody perennial shrub, with all flowers perfect and fertile; western. Fig. 356 . . . . .SAGE-BRUSH, *Artemisia tridentata* Nutt.

Native perennial, with silvery-gray hairs 1—10 ft. high. Leaves wedge shaped with 3—7 blunt teeth at apex, as pictured, ½—1½ in. long. Heads with 5—8 flowers, numerous, about ⅛ in. across. Achenes light yellow.

Abundant in dry places throughout the great plains and western regions. July—Sept.

Other names: Mountain Sage, Sage-wood.

Figure 356

31b Herbaceous plants, with glabrous leaves .32

32a Leaves with rounded lobes; heads in open spreading panicles; plants sweet scented. Fig. 357.................................
.................ANNUAL WORMWOOD, *Artemesia annua* L.

Eurasian annual, much branched, 2—5 ft. high. Leaves 2—3 times pinnately divided 1—6 in. long. Heads drooping very numerous, about ⅛ in. or smaller in diameter, in large, spreading panicles; flowers greenish; achenes light yellow.

An escaped ornamental, often common in waste places and fields. July—Sept.

Figure 357

32b Leaves with pointed lobes; heads in axillary clusters, as pictured (a). Fig. 358...BIENNIAL WORMWOOD, *Artemesia biennis* Willd.

Native annual or biennial, branched, with numerous leaves, 1—4 ft. high. Leaves 1—2 times pinnately divided, 1—4 in. long. Heads standing erect, about 1/6 in. in diameter; flowers yellowish or purplish; achenes brown.

Common, especially westward, in fields and waste places. Aug. —Sept.

Other names: Bitterweed, False-tansy.

Figure 358

33a At least some parts of the plant (usually the under side of the leaves) densely white-woolly; leaves entire or with wavy margins 34

33b Plants not at all densely white-woolly but either glabrous or pubescent; leaves toothed or cut. Fig. 359.........................
......................FIRE-WEED, *Erechtites hieracifolia* (L.)

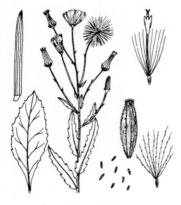

Native annual with grooved, succulent stems 1—7 ft. high. Leaves thin, 1—8 in. long. Heads ½—¾ in. high, noticeably swollen at the base; flowers greenish-white. Achenes narrow, flattened, with 10 ribs, dark brown; pappus white.

One of the first plants to appear in burned-over areas. Aug.—Sept.

Other name: Pilewort.

Figure 359

34a Basal leaves absent or much the same as the stem leaves.....35

34b Basal leaves wider and larger than the stem leaves. Fig. 360....
..............INDIAN TOBACCO, *Antennaria plantaginifolia* (L.)

Native perennial spreading by rootstocks and forming dense patches, thickly covered with white wool; flowering stocks 3—20 in. high. Leaves silvery beneath, mostly in a rosette at base, 1—3 in. long and up to 1½ in. wide; stem leaves small, narrow and widely scattered. Heads dioecious about ¼ in. across, with many whitish flowers; the sterile plants and heads are noticably smaller than the fertile ones.

Common in dry pastures and fields, often on poor soil. April—May.

Figure 360

Other names: Ladies Tobacco, Early Everlasting, Plantain-leaved Everlasting, Mouse-ears, Pussy-toes.

Several other species of the genus, often smaller, may act as weeds on worn or acid soils. *Antennaria neglecta* Greene is very common. Its leaves are small and narrow as compared with *plantaginifolia*.

35a Both stamens and pistils on the same plant; bracts of the involucre brownish or yellowish.......................................36

35b Stamens on one plant; pistils on another plant (dioecious); bracts of the involucre pearly-white. Fig. 361..........................
.............PEARLY EVERLASTING, *Anaphalis margaritacea* (L.)

Native perennial, stem covered with tangled, white wool, 1—3 ft. high. Leaves linear, 3—5 in. long, heavy tomentose below. Heads numerous, about 1/3 in. across and with pearly-white bracts, and many whitish flowers. Achenes tiny, cylindrical, yellowish-brown.

Often common on stony or sandy soil. Aug.—Sept.

Other names: Cotton - w e e d, Ladies-tobacco, Silver-leaf, Poverty-weed, Silver-button, I n d i a n - posy, Moonshine.

Figure 361

36a Plants less than 12 in. high, loosely branched and spreading; heads mostly terminal. Fig. 362....................................
....................LOW CUDWEED, *Gnaphalium uliginosum* L.

Native annual, often diffused, with stems 2—8 in. long. Leaves sessile, covered with dense white wool, ½—1½ in. long. Heads about 1/6 in. across, several in terminal bunches; flowers, whitish, about 1/12 in. high; achenes very small, light brown.

In pastures and fields, ranging above the middle of the United States. July—Sept.

Other names: Mouse-ear, Wartwort, Marsh-cudweed.

Figure 362

36b Plant more than a foot high; erect. Fig. 363.....................
...................SWEET BALSAM, *Gnaphalium obtusifolium* L.

Figure 363

Native annual or winter annual, tomentose, fragrant 1—3 ft. high. Leaves with tapering base, not decurrent, white-woolly beneath, often dark green above, 1—3 in. long. Heads slender, about 1/5 in. high, many flowered; bracts numerous, white. Flowers white; achenes pale brown.

Often common in waste places, fields, etc. Aug.—Sept.

Other names: Fragrant Life-everlasting, White Balsam, Rabbit-tobacco, Fussy gussy, Feather-weed, Chafe-weed, Old-field Balsam.

CLAMMY EVERLASTING, *G. macounii* Green is similar in size and range but has decurrent leaves and sticky pubescence on the stems.

37a Receptacle covered with dense bristles; bracts deeply fringed (a) or with slender hooked tips (b). Fig. 364..............38

Figure 364

37b Receptacle naked; bracts neither deeply fringed nor with hooked ʾr spiny tips. Fig. 365......................................
...................TALL IRONWEED, *Vernonia altissima* Nutt.

Figure 365

Native perennial, usually, with sturdy erect stems 4—10 ft. high. Leaves finely serrate, up to 1 ft. long and 1½ in. wide. Heads about ¼ in. across with 15—30 reddish-purple flowers; pappus purplish.

On low ground in pastures and waste places.

Several other species of this genus are found in pastures and along water courses, all in general characters somewhat like *altissima* but usually less robust.

173

38a Bracts deeply fringed or with straight spines; leaves elongate, at least some of them usually deeply pinnately cut............39

38b Bracts with hooked tips (a); leaves broad, often cordate at the base. Fig. 366........SMALLER BURDOCK, *Arctium minus* **(Hill)**

European biennial with fleshy tap root, erect, branching 2—5 ft. high. Leaves felty, pale and more canescent on under side, 3—15 in. long; all first year leaves arising from the ground. Heads usually less than 1 in. in diameter, borne in axillary racemes; the bracts with numerous barb-tipps to readily adhere to other heads or to passing animals. Flowers tubular, pinkish-purple or occasionally white. Ripened burs remaining pretty much intact for a time, thus aiding in seed distribution. Achenes mottled brown about 1/6 in. long.

Figure 366

Common in neglected rich soil of barnyards and fields. July—Nov. Other names: Clotbur, Cuckoo-button, Common Burdock.

GREAT BURDOCK, *A. lappa* L. closely resembles the above, but is larger in about every detail. It may attain a height of 8 or 9 ft. and possess leaves nearly 2 ft. long.

39a Bracts of involucre tipped with sharp, yellow spines (a); flowers yellow. Fig. 367....BARNABY'S THISTLE, *Centaurea solstitialis* **L.**

European annual with stiff, spreading branches and thick, gray pubescence, 1—2 ft. high. Basal leaves pinnately cut, 3—6 in. long; stem leaves linear, small. Heads solitary, terminal about 1 in. across, with spines and yellow tubular flowers, as pictured. Achenes light brown, with bristly pappus.

Widely scattered in waste land and cultivated fields. July—Sept.

Other name: Yellow Star-thistle.

Figure 367

174

39b Bracts fringed, flowers other than yellow. (See Fig. 368a)......40

40a (b, c) Leaves with slender pinnate lobes, as pictured; heads numerous. Fig. 368....*SPOTTED KNAPWEED, Centaurea maculosa* Lam.

European biennial, spreading by creeping roots, often with many stiff branches, 1½—3 ft. high. Leaves 1—3 in. long. Heads both terminal and axillary, ½—¾ in. across, flowers pink to purple (rarely white), those at the margin larger. Achenes brownish.

In waste and cultivated ground, especially where dry. July—Sept.

Figure 368

40b Leaves slender grass-like (lower ones sometimes weakly toothed); heads solitary on slender stems; marginal flowers much larger than central ones. Fig. 369...CORN FLOWER, *Centaurea cyanus* L.

European annual or winter annual, grayish green with soft pubescence, 1—3 ft. high. Leaves, as pictured, 2—6 in. long. Heads 1—1½ in. across, with conspicuous, deeply-cut, tubular, marginal flowers. Flowers normally blue but frequently varying to pink, purple, or white, the outer ones very showy but with neither stamens nor pistil. Achenes mottled yellow and brown up to 1/6 in. long.

Much raised as an ornamental from which it escapes to become a weed pest. July—Sept.

Figure 369

Other names: Bachelor's-button, Blue-bottle, Blue-poppy, Blue-caps, French-pink.

40c Upper leaves entire, lanceolate; lower ones tooth or pinnately lobed; heads solitary on leafy branches. Fig. 370..............
..................**RUSSIAN KNAPWEED,** *Centaurea repens* **L.**

Asiatic perennial with creeping roots, grows erect to a height of 1—3 ft. Leaves, entire above, coarsely toothed or pinnately lobed on lower parts of plant. Heads ½—¾ in. across, with many rose, blue or purple flowers. Achenes striated, brownish, about 1/10 in. long.

In waste ground, fields, and meadows. June—Sept.

Other name: T u r k e s t a n Thistle.

Figure 370

41a Heads rarely over 1 in. across; leaves dark green both sides; plants spreading by underground rootstocks. Fig. 371.................
......................**CANADA THISTLE,** *Circium arvense* **(L.)**

European perennial, growing vigorously in patches, 1—3 ft. high. Leaves sessile, slightly clasping, variously lobed 3—8 in. long. Heads numerous, about 1 in. high, and wide; flowers reddish-purple, occasionally white. Achenes brown, somewhat flattened and sometimes curved; about ⅛ in. long.

A persistent weed wherever it becomes established, in waste places, pastures, fields, etc. July —Oct.

Other names: Creeping Thistle, Cursed Thistle, Corn Thistle, Small-flowered Thistle, G r e e n Thistle.

Figure 371

41b Heads 1½ in. or more across; without spreading rootstocks....42

42a Base of leaf running down plant stem below the point of attachment (decurrent); spines tipping all of the involucral bracts. Fig. 372.....................BULL THISTLE, *Circium vulgare* **(Savi.)**

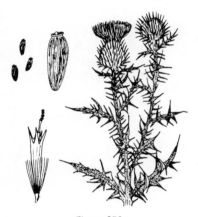

Figure 372

Eurasian biennial, growing from a thick taproot, woolly stems, 3—5 ft. high. Leaves with spine tipped lobes, rough above, covered with brownish hairs beneath, 2—6 in. long. Heads usually solitary at the end of a branch up to 2 in. across and high; flowers reddish-purple, the outer ones often darker. Achenes yellowish-brown, about 1/10 in. long, pappus plumose.

Very common and widely distributed in pastures, fields, and neglected land. The first year appearing as a large flattened rosette. July—Nov.

Other names: Spear Thistle, Bur Thistle, Plume Thistle, Road-side Thistle.

42b Leaves not decurrent on stem, white tomentose below; only the outer involucral bracts spine tipped. Fig. 373...................
........................TALL THISTLE, *Circium altissimum* **(L.)**

Figure 373

Native biennial, stem heavy branched, 3—10 ft. high. Leaves white-woolly on under side, sometimes lobed but often only dentate 3—8 in. long. Heads solitary on the ends of branches 1½—2 in. high and wide; flowers rather uniformly rose-purple. Achenes yellowish brown, about 1/5 in. long.

Common and widely distributed in pastures and waste land, seeming to prefer wet land. Aug.—Oct.

Other name: Roadside Thistle.

Several other species of thistles similar to this and the preceding are sometimes found as weeds.

43a Heads nodding as pictured; involucre about 1½ in. in diameter. Fig. 374.....................MUSK-THISTLE, *Carduus nutans* L.

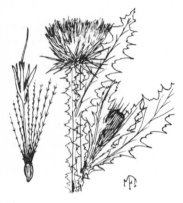

European biennial, 1½—3 ft. high. Leaves 3—6 in. long, with many prickles. Flower fragrant, purple (occasionally white); pappus bristles about 1 in. long, very minutely barbed, white; achenes brown to olive, about 1/6 in. long.

In Central and Northeastern States and in Canada; in waste land, pastures, etc. June—Oct.

Other names: Buck Thistle, Plumeless Thistle, Queen Anne's Thistle, Nodding Thistle.

Figure 374

43b Heads erect; involucre smaller, about ½ in. in diameter. Fig. 375 ....WELTED THISTLE, *Carduus crispus* L.

European biennial, 2—4 ft. high. Leaves very spiny, with wavy margins. Heads in groups of several, rather small; flowers purple or white.

Roadsides, waste land, and fields, from Missouri north and eastward to the Atlantic. June—Oct.

Other name: Curled Thistle.

Figure 375

44a Pappus, at least of the disk-flowers, of slender hair-like bristles (a); ray-flowers, pistillate (without anthers or pollen). Fig. 376.......................58

Figure 376

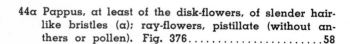

44b Pappus none (a) or sometimes represented by
a crown (b), a few awns (c), chaffy scales, or
minute bristles. Fig. 377 45

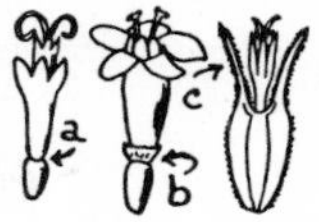

Figure 377

45a (b, c) Pappus of awns. Fig. 377c 46

45b Pappus of scales 47

45c Pappus none, or a crown 52

46a Pappus of disk-flowers of 2 or 3 stiff awns (a); heads very resinous
and sticky; all flowers yellow; receptacle naked. Fig. 378 . . . . . .
. . . . . . BROAD-LEAVED GUM-PLANT, *Grindelia squarrosa* (Pursh)

Native biennial or perennial;
erect 1—3 ft. high. Stems glabrous, branched and frequently
reddish. Leaves sessile, often
clasping, stiff, 1—3 in. long.
Heads terminal, solitary, involucre glutinous, the tips of the
bracts strongly r e c u r v e d ;
achenes about ⅛ in. long, gray
or grayish brown, awns 2 to 8.

Dry pastures and waste
places. Aug.—Oct.

Other names: Gumweed, Ro-
sin-weed, Stickly-head, T a r -
weed.

Figure 378

46b Heads scarcely if at all sticky, awns 2—4, at least the ray-flowers
yellow . . . . SPANISH NEEDLES, page 194

47a Receptacle chaffy 50

47b Receptacle naked; disk globular 48

48a Leaves very narrow, as pictured. Fig. 379.......................
........FINE-LEAVED SNEEZEWEED, *Helenium tenuifolium* Nutt.

Native annual with slender, usually glabrous stem up to 2 ft. in height. Leaves all linear-filiform ½—1½ in. long. Heads ¾—1 in. across; disk yellow; rays 4—8, with 3—4 teeth.

In meadows, pastures, and waste land. Aug.—Oct.

Other names: Yellow Dog Fennel, Bitterweed.

Figure 379

48b Stem leaves broadened.....................................**49**

49a Disk brown or purplish; rays sterile, stem and leaves entire. Fig. 380.....PURPLE-HEAD SNEEZEWEED, *Helenium nudiflorum* Nutt.

Native perennial with slender, puberulent stems up to 3 ft. high. Stem leaves mostly lanceolate 1—3 in. long. Heads 1—1½ in. across; rays 10—15 (rarely none), wholly yellow, or with brown at base, or wholly brown; 3 toothed.

In moist places, along ditches, in pastures, etc. June—Oct.

Figure 380

49b Disk yellow; rays fertile; stem-leaves toothed. Fig. 381..........
........................SNEEZEWEED, *Helenium autumnale* L.

Native perennial with rather heavy stem 2—5 ft. high. Leaves rather stiff 2—5 in. long. Heads many, 1—2 in. across; disk yellow; rays 10—18 bright yellow, with 3 teeth.

In swamps and damp pastures, etc. Aug.—Oct.

Other names: Ox-eye, False Sunflower, Staggerwort, Swamp Sunflower, Yellow-star.

Figure 381

50a Leaves deeply pinnately divided, pappus scales (about 10) cut beyond middle into many bristle-like parts. Fig. 382............
...................FETID MARIGOLD, *Dyssodia papposa* (Vent.)

Native annual, much branched, glabrous or with fine pubescence, ½—1½ ft. high. Leaves finely cut, as pictured, ½—2 in. long; with strong odor. Heads many, less than ½ in. across; bracts purplish, in one row; ray-flowers few, disk-flowers many, both yellow. Achenes blackish, about 1/6 in. long.

In fields and waste places. June—Oct.

Other names: Stinkweed, False Dog-fennel, False May-weed.

Figure 382

50b Leaves entire or only toothed..............................51

51a The 4—5 broad ray-flowers white; heads less than ½ in. across. Fig. 383.....................GALINSOGA, *Galinsoga ciliata* **Blake**

Annual introduced from Tropical America, weak stemmed, heavily pubescent, 1—2 ft. high. Leaves, coarsely toothed, ¾—3 in. long; the 4 or 5 ray flowers white, about 2 mm. long and nearly the same width.

A very common and highly persistent weed, maturing quickly. May—Nov.

Other name: French weed.

G. *parviflora* Cav. similar to *ciliata* differs in the pappus of the disk flowers having no awns and the ray flowers being without pappus.

Figure 383

G. *caracasana* (DC.) occurs as a weed from Mass. to Va. It can be distinguished by its purple rays.

51b Ray-flowers yellow; pappus 2—4 deciduous awns, not barbed.... ....SUNFLOWERS, page 197

52a Receptacle chaffy; ray-flowers yellow or white................54

52b Receptacle naked; ray-flowers white, pink, or purple..........53

53a Low plants with only basal leaves, as pictured. Fig. 384....... ....ENGLISH DAISY, *Bellis perennis* **L.**

European perennial. Stems 2—8 in. high, leafless, bearing a solitary head; leaves basal, 1—2 in. long, with long hairs and feeble dentations; heads ½—1 in. across with numerous white, pink, or purple rays and yellow disk-flowers.

An escaped ornamental in pastures, lawns, etc., widely scattered. April—Nov.

Other names: Lawn Daisy, Marguerite, Bonewort, Hen-and-chickens, Herb Margaret.

Figure 384

53b Plants with leafy stems and large heads; ray-flowers white. Fig. 385............**OX-EYE DAISY,** *Chrysanthemum leucanthemum* **L.**

European perennial. Stems erect, 1—3 ft. high, leaves 1—3 in. long, the basal ones often with long petioles; heads solitary or few 1—2 in. across or larger; ray-flowers white, disk-flowers yellow. The variety *pinnatifidum*, with pinnate leaves, seems to be more abundant and more widely distributed.

Meadow, roadsides, pastures, etc. June—Aug.

Other names: White-weed, Marguerite, Field D a i s y , Poorland Flower.

Figure 385

55a Leaves pinnately divided; rays 1—3 in. in length. Fig. 386......
........**GRAY-HEADED CONE-FLOWER,** *Ratibida pinnata* **(Vent.)**

Native perennial. Rough and with appressed pubescence, 3 —5 ft. high. Leaves alternate, 3—7 divided, up to 10 in. long. Heads solitary on long stems; ray-flowers 4—10, y e l l o w , drooping; disk, as pictured, gray changing to b r o w n ; achenes grayish-black, without pappus.

Meadows, pastures, a n d waste land; a prairie plant spreading eastward. June— Sept.

Figure 386

Other names: Cone-headed Daisy, Prairie Cone-flower.

55b Leaves simple. Fig. 387..BLACK-EYED SUSAN, *Rudbeckia hirta* **L.**

Native biennial. R o u g h , hairy, erect, 1—3 ft. high. Leaves, 2—7 in. long and up to 2 in. wide, thick and rough, entire or with shallow serrations. Rays 10—20, orange-yellow, 1—1½ in. long; disk-flowers, many, perfect, dark purplish-brown; achenes black, without pappus.

Often frequent in fields and meadows. June—Oct.

Other names: Yellow Daisy, Cone-flower, English Bull's-eye, Nigger-head, Ox-eye D a i s y , Golden Jerusalem.

Figure 387

56a Heads small and many in compact clusters. Fig. 388 . . . .
. . . . . YARROW, *Achillea millefolium* **L.**

European perennial. S t e m simple or somewhat branched above, 1—2 ft. high. Leaves alternate, very finely cut, up to 10 in. long. Young plants in a rosette, sometimes mistaken for a fern. Heads densely placed in flat-topped corymbs. Ray-flowers, 5—10, white; disk-flowers white. (Form *rosea* has ray flowers, pink to rose-purple.)

Common in pastures, meadows, and waste land. June—Sept.

Other names: Milfoil, Bloodwort, Thousand-leaf, Old Man's Pepper.

Figure 388

56b Heads solitary, ½ in. or more across 57

57a Ill-scented; ray-flowers neutral. Fig. 389......................
............................**DOG FENNEL**, *Anthemis cotula* **L.**

European annual. Much branched, bushy plant 1—2 ft. high; highly scented. Leaves alternate, sessile, finely cut; heads solitary, up to 1 in. or more in diameter; ray-flowers 15—30 white, sterile. Disk-flowers yellow, perfect.

Often very abundant in barnlots and waste land. June—Oct.

Other names: Mayweed, Stinkweed, Fetid Chamomile, Stinking Daisy.

Figure 389

57b Without odor; ray-flowers, seed-bearing. Fig. 390..............
....................**CORN CHAMOMILE**, *Anthemis arvensis* **L.**

European biennial. Much branched, about 1 ft. high. Leaves alternate and fine cut, 1—2 in. long; ray-flowers 12—20, white, pistillate; disk-flowers yellow, perfect.

In fields and waste land. Mar.—Aug.

Other names: Field Chamomile, Field Dog-fennel.

Figure 390

58a Ray-flowers not yellow.....................................**59**

58b Ray-flowers yellow or cream colored........................**64**

59a Scales of involucre (a) in several rows and lengths, overlapping. Fig. 391a....................................**ASTERS, page 190**

59b Scales of involucre (a) in but 1 or 2 rows, narrow and scarcely overlapping. Fig. 391b....**60**

Figure 391

60a Heads very small and numerous, rays inconspicuous, scarcely longer than the pappus. Fig. 392.............................
.........................HORSE-WEED, *Erigeron canadensis* L.

Figure 392

Native annual. Usually hairy, 1—8 ft. high; leaves alternate, the lower ones often spatulate and with petioles and teeth; upper leaves lanceolate to linear, sessile and mostly entire. Disk-flowers yellow, numerous, perfect; ray-flowers, greenish white, but little if any longer than the disk-flowers. Achenes about 1/25 in. long, flattened.

A common, widely distributed and persistent weed, in meadows, fields, and pastures. June—Nov.

Other names: Colt's-tail, Mare's-tail, Hog-weed, Butter-weed, Bitterweed, Fireweed, Canada Fleabane.

Other similar weeds are the LOW HORSE-WEED *E. divaricatus* Michx., a low, (¼—1 ft. high) much branched plant (native) and *E. bonariensis* L. a tropical weed found in Fla., Calif., and some other southern states which may be recognized by its dense covering of ash-gray bristles.

60b Rays long and slender, white or colored......................**61**

61a Heads 1 inch or more in diameter; ray-flowers about 50, blue. Fig. 393..............ROBIN'S-PLANTAIN, *Erigeron pulchellus* Michx.

Native perennial. Simple, erect, stems 1—2 ft. high; leaves alternate entire or with small dentations, heavily covered with sticky hairs. Heads few 1—1½ in. across; ray-flowers blue or purplish, pistillate; disk-flowers greenish yellow, numerous, perfect.

Widely distributed in pastures and meadows. April—July.

Other names: Blue Spring Daisy, Rose-petty, Robert's Plantain.

Figure 393

61b Heads smaller, about ¾ in. or less across...................62

62a Heads with about 50 white or whitish ray-flowers; leaves not clasping..63

62b Heads with 100 or more pink ray-flowers; leaves clasping. Fig. 394.......PHILADELPHIA FLEABANE, *Erigeron philadelphicus* L.

Native perennial. Slender, pubescent stems, usually branched above, 1—3 ft. high. Leaves alternate and mostly simple, 1—3 in. long. Heads rather numerous; disk-flowers many, perfect, yellow; ray-flowers 100—150, pistillate, pinkish to rose-red.

Widely distributed, in pastures, meadows, etc. April—Aug.

Other names: Skevish, Daisy-Fleabane, Sweet Scabiosus.

Figure 394

63a Stem leaves mostly with sharp teeth; stem with spreading hairs. Fig. 395.....................WHITE-TOP, *Erigeron annuus* (L.)

Figure 395

Native annual (or biennial). Stems coarse, hispid, spreading, 1—4 ft. high; leaves 2—6 in. long and up to 3 in. in width, coarsely toothed. Heads with 40—70 rays, usually white but often tinted with lavender; disk-flowers yellow.

Almost cosmopolitan; frequent in meadows, fields and waste places. June—Oct.

Other names: White - w e e d , Daisy Fleabane, Sweet Scabiosus.

63b Stem leaves linear, mostly without teeth on margins; stem with appressed hairs. Fig. 396...................................... ....DAISY-FLEABANE, *Erigeron strigosus* Muhl.

Figure 396

Native annual or biennial. Stems erect, with appressed hairs, 1—4 ft. high. Stem leaves narrow and usually entire, basal leaves spatulate or oblong 2—5 in. long. Ray-flowers white or occasionally purplish; disk flowers yellow.

Widely scattered over much of our country in meadows and waste land. June—Sept.

Other names: Rough Daisy-fleabane, White-top.

Figure 397

64a Bracts of involucre in but one series. Fig. 397a..65

Figure 398

64b Bracts of involucre in 3 or more series. Fig. 398a 66

65a Stem slender bearing a solitary head; basal leaves orbicular with long petiole. Fig. 399..........COLTSFOOT, *Tussilago farfara* L.

Figure 399

European perennial. Scaly stems coming up in early spring from the underground rootstocks, at first woolly, 1/3 —1½ ft. high. Leaves basal, palmately v e i n e d , 3—7 in. across, densely covered below with white tomentose. Heads about 1 in. across, solitary; both ray- and disk-flowers bright yellow; achenes ⅛ in. long with many vertical ribs.

Spreading in our North East, along water ways and in fields. March—June.

O t h e r names: Horse-hoof, Ass's-foot, Bull's-foot, Sow-foot, Clay-weed, Butter-bur.

65b Stems hollow, branching into many heads; leaves pinnately lobed (see fig. 354). COMMON GROUNDSEL......................29c

66a Heads very numerous, small, less than ½ in. across, bracts in several series, overlapping (a). Fig. 400. ....GOLDENRODS, page 191

Figure 400

66b Heads few, 2 in. or more across. Fig. 401.....................
..............................ELECAMPANE, *Inula helenium* L.

Eurasian perennial. H e a v y , erect stems, 2—6 ft. high, pubescent and sometimes branching. Leaves up to 20 in. long and 8 in. wide, rough above, pubescent on under side.

Heads 2—4 in. across, all flowers yellow; achenes smooth, 4-sided.

In fields, along road-sides, and waste land throughout much of the eastern half of our region. July—Sept.

Other names: Wild Sunflower, Horseheal, Elf-dock, S c a b w o r t, Yellow Starwort, Horse-elder.

Figure 401

ASTERS

Many species of this large genus abound in pastures, waste land, etc., but ordinarily do not offer serious problems of eradication. They contribute a sizable percentage of our fall-flowering native plants. All of the more than a hundred American species with their white, pink, lavender, and purple flowers, are interesting and many of them truly beautiful. Since they are not serious weeds, we show only a few.

1a Rays white 2
1b Ray purple (sometimes rose or pink); heads 1 in. or more across; leaves clasping. Fig. 402....................................
.................NEW ENGLAND ASTER, *Aster novae-angliae* L.

Native perennial. Stem robust, with dense, sticky pubescence, 2—8 ft. high; leaves with cordate base, 2—5 in. long; ray-flowers 40—50 violet- or deep-purple (sometimes white, pink, or rose, especially in cultivation).

Widely distributed in pastures and roadsides. Aug.—Oct.

Figure 402

2a Plant standing stiffly erect, 1—3 ft. high; heads about ½ in. across, disk-flowers yellow. Fig. 403.....................................
.......................WHITE-HEATH ASTER, *Aster ericoides* L.

Native perennial. Erect, bushy plant 1—3 ft. high; leaves 1—3 in. long, the lower ones spatulate, stem leaves linear or nearly so. Ray-flowers 10—20 usually white, occasionally bluish.

Widely distributed in fields and waste land. July—Oct.

Other names: Frost weed, Steel weed, Michaelmas Daisy.

Aster multiflorus Ait. DENSE-FLOWERED ASTER, a low spreading plant with very numerous tiny heads is by Gray considered a synonym of *ericoides*.

Figure 403

2b Stems slender to 4 ft. long, arched or reclining; rays white or occasionally pinkish; disk-flowers purplish. Fig. 404...............
...........................CALICO ASTER, *Aster lateriflorus* L.

Native perennial. Spreading or reclining; leaves lanceolate, serrate, 2—5 in. long and up to 1 in. wide. Heads usually numerous, on one side of the stem, ¼ to ½ in. across, disk flowers lavender to purple, darkening with age. It is a rather highly variable species with 3 varieties named.

Common and widely distributed; roadsides, waste land, etc. Aug.—Oct.

Other names: Starved Aster, Maryland Rosemary.

Figure 404

GOLDENRODS

This genus like the asters has many quite similar species. A large number behave as weeds at times but we are showing only a few species. Excepting two or three species in which the ray-flowers are pale cream colored and an occasional albino form, all of the some 100 American species have bright yellow rays.

1a Rays more numerous than the disk-flowers; heads sessile or nearly so; leaves narrow and entire. Fig. 405 . . . .
. . . .**BUSHY GOLDENROD,** *Solidago graminifolia* **(L.)**

Native perennial. Stems much-branched to form a flat-topped corymb; 2—4 ft. high. Leaves linear with 3—5 ribs 1—5 in. long; ray-flowers 12—20, disk-flowers 8—12, all yellow. Several varieties have been named.

Common in moist fields, and roadsides. July—Oct.

Other names: Flat-topped Goldenrod, Fragrant Goldenrod.

Figure 405

1b Ray-flowers usually fewer than the disk-flowers; heads usually with stems, not sessile **2**

2a Heads in a flat-topped inflorescence; leaves thick, stiff and often clasping and entire. Fig. 406 . . . .
. . . .**STIFF-LEAVED GOLDENROD,** *Solidago rigida* **L.**

Native perennial. Heavy, usually simple stem 1—5 ft. high, leaves hoary, thick, rigid; those of the stem usually clasping, and 1—2 in. long; basal leaves often with long petioles and measuring up to 3 in. wide and a foot in length. Heads showy with 30—40 flowers, only 6—10 of which are rays.

Widely distributed in poor dry soil and readily recognized. Aug.—Oct.

Other name: Hard-leaved Goldenrod.

Figure 406

2b Heads in a terminal spreading panicle, frequently with recurving branches 3

3a Leaves with 3 longitudinal veins (a); heads numerous and very small 1/10 in. or less in height. Fig. 407....................... ....CANADA GOLDENROD, *Solidago canadensis* L.

Native perennial. Stem slender, usually glabrous, 1—5 ft. high; leaves many and crowded, with 3 veins and usually sharp serrations, 2—5 in. long. Ray-flowers very short, and but few (4—6); achenes pubescent.

Widely distributed and quite variable in waste land, roadsides, etc. Aug.—Oct.

Other names: Tall Goldenrod, Rock Goldenrod.

Figure 407

3b Leaves pinnately veined (a), sharply serrate and usually pubescent; stem heavily pubescent. Fig. 408............................... ....TALL HAIRY GOLDENROD, *Solidago rugosa* Ait.

Native perennial. Stem simple or branched, villous, 1—7 ft. high; leaves pubescent or scabrous, 1—4 in. long; ray-flowers 6—9, disk flowers 4—7. Several varieties have been named.

In dry fields and waste land. Aug.—Oct.

Other names: Pyramid Goldenrod, Bitterweed, Rough Goldenrod.

Figure 408

193

SPANISH NEEDLES

The members of this genus (*Bidens*) are well known for their cling-ing seeds, frequently of "boot-jack" type. Creek bottoms and other low lands are often thickly covered with these plants. The display they make when in bloom in the fall is truly remarkable.

1a Ray-flowers conspicuous. (See Fig. 415).........................5

1b Ray-flowers absent, rudimentary or very short. (See Figs. 411-413).2

2a Leaves pinnately divided. Fig. 409.............3

Figure 409

2b Leaves mostly lanceolate. Fig. 410.......4

Figure 410

3a Achenes ("seeds") linear (a). Fig. 411...........................
.........................SPANISH-NEEDLES, *Bidens bipinnata* L.

Figure 411

Native annual. Stems square, erect, glabrous 1—6 ft. high; leaves opposite, 3—5 pinnately divided; heads many, few flow-ered; bracts few, the outer ones frequently leaf-like; ray-flowers very short or absent; achenes needle-like.

Common and widely distributed in waste land, fields, and gardens. Aug.—Oct.

Other name: Cuckolds.

3b Achenes flattened (a). Fig. 412. ....
............................BEGGAR-TICKS, *Bidens frondosa* L.

Native annual. Stems erect, rather slender, often purplish, 1—3 ft. high. Leaves, 3—5 divided, thin 2—4 in. long. Heads many on long pedicels, ½ inch or more across, bracts 5—8, leaf-like, rays none or quite inconspicuous, disk-flowers orange.

Roadsides, pastures, waste land, etc. Aug.—Oct.

Other names: Stick-tights, Devil's Boot-jack, Pitchfork-weed, Bur-marigold.

Figure 412

4a Heads always erect; disk-flowers orange, stems purple. Fig. 413...
..PURPLE-STEMMED SWAMP BEGGAR-TICK, *Bidens connata* Muhl.

Native annual. Stems purple, erect, glabrous up to 8 ft. in height. Leaves with coarse, sharp serrations, 2—5 in. long. Heads ½—1½ in. across, rays few and inconspicuous or none; disk flowers orange.

Often abundant in ditches and other wet places. Highly variable with a number of named varieties. Aug.—Oct.

Other names: Stick-tight, Pitchforks, Harvest Lice.

Figure 413

4b Heads nodding after the flowers mature; leaves sessile or united at their base; rays if present shorter than the bracts of the involucre. Fig. 414............NODDING BUR-MARIGOLD, Bidens cernua L.

Native annual. Stem usually erect, 2—3 ft. high. Leaves sessile, s o m e t i m e s perfoliate, coarsely serrate, 3—6 in. long; heads hemispherical, with 6— 10 short rays or sometimes none. Achenes wedge-shaped and usually with 4 awns.

A widely distributed weed, especially in wet places. Several v a r i e t i e s have been named. Aug.—Oct.

Figure 414

5a Leaves mostly pinnately divided; achenes pubescent...........6

5b Leaves lanceolate. Fig. 415....................................
....................LARGER BUR-MARIGOLD, Bidens laevis (L.)

Native annual or perennial. Stem erect, smooth, 1—3 ft. high. Leaves sessile, 3—8 in. long and up to 1 in. wide. Heads numerous, 1—2½ in. across; rays 8—10, golden yellow and very showy. Achenes wedge-shaped; awns shorter than the achene.

Abundant and widely distributed in wet places. Aug. —Oct.

Other names: Smooth Bur-Marigold, Brook Sunflower.

Figure 415

6a Achenes much flattened, awns 2—4, nearly as long as the achenes. Fig. 416 ....
......WESTERN TICKSEED-SUNFLOWER, *Bidens aristosa* (Michx.)

Figure 416

Native annual or biennial. Stem erect, much branched, 1—3 ft. high. Leaves thin, with pubescence on under side 3—7 divided and up to 6 in. long. Heads on slender stems, 1—2 in. across; rays 6—9, ending bluntly; achenes much flattened.

In swamps and wet land. Aug. —Oct. Three varieties have been named.

6b Achenes wedge-shaped or somewhat linear and bearing ciliated shorter ear-like awns (a). Fig. 417 ....
....................TICKSEED-SUNFLOWER, *Bidens coronata* (L.)

Figure 417

Native annual or biennial. Stem slender, erect, 2—5 ft. high. Leaves 3—7 divided, 2—8 in. long. Heads many, up to 2½ in. across; rays 6-18, golden yellow. Several varieties have been named for this variable species.

Widely distributed in wet places. Aug.—Oct.

SUNFLOWERS

Sunflowers and Spanish Needles dominate the fall landscape in many places. They are persistent weeds but make a beautiful display. There are many species; only a few are shown here.

**1a Disk dark brown or purplish; upper leaves alternate. Fig. 418. . . .
. . . . .COMMON SUNFLOWER, *Helianthus annuus* L.**

Native annual. Stem usually simple, heavy, erect, 3—7
ft. high. Leaves broad cordate-
ovate with long petiole, up to
12 in. or more in length. Heads,
solitary, when growing wild
3—6 in. across; disk brownish
or purplish, rays orange-yellow;
achenes usually mottled gray,
fleshy.

This plant is often cultivated
for its seed or as an ornamental but grows as a weed in
fields, roadsides, and waste
land. Aug.—Oct.

Other names: Wild Sunflower, Comb Flower.

Figure 418

1b Disk yellow or yellowish. 2

2a Leaves narrowly-lanceolate 3

**2b Leaves ovate or ovate-lanceolate and with long petioles. Fig. 419. .
. . . . .JERUSALEM ARTICHOKE, *Helianthus tuberosus* L.**

Native perennial, with elongate rhizomes which enlarge at
their tips into fleshy, edible
tubers. Stem usually branching, 5—10 ft. high. Leaves
roughened above, pubescent
beneath, 4—8 in. long. Ray-
flowers 12—20, bright yellow,
giving the head a diameter of
2—3½ in; disk ½ in. across;
achenes pubescent.

Frequently cultivated for the
tubers, escaping to damp waste
land. Aug.—Oct.

Other names: Earth Apple,
Canada Potato, Girasole.

Figure 419

3a Leaves sessile or nearly so; stem roughened. Fig. 420............
...................**GIANT SUNFLOWER**, *Helianthus giganteus* **L.**

Native perennial. Stem usually purple and branching above, 3—12 ft. high. Leaves lanceolate, firm, much roughened above, pinnately veined 4—10 in. long. Heads solitary or few at branch tips; ray-flowers 10—20 pale yellow.

In swamps and damp fields. July—Oct.

Other names: Tall Sunflower, Wild Sunflower.

Figure 420

3b Leaves with long petioles; stem smooth and waxy. Fig. 421......
SAW-TOOTHED SUNFLOWER, *Helianthus grosseserratus* **Martens**

Native perennial. Stems coarse and smooth 5—12 ft. high. Leaves alternate, coarsely toothed, harshly roughened above, covered with whitish pubescence beneath. Heads up to 3 in. in diameter; rays 10—20 deep yellow. Achenes nearly smooth.

Along roadsides and in rich waste land. July—Oct.

Figure 421

WEEDS ARRANGED IN THEIR BOTANICAL ORDER

Botanists do not altogether agree on the orderly relationship of plants. The weeds described in this book are being placed in a commonly accepted arrangement. This list should give excellent ideas of relationship and provide a checklist for marking or reference.

FUNGI

Poisonous Mushrooms	*Aminita* spp.
Ergot	*Claviceps purpurea* Tul.

FERNS

Field Horsetail	*Equisetum arvense* L.
Bracken Fern	*Pteridium aquilinum* (L.)

MONOCOTYLEDONS

CAT-TAIL FAMILY, *Typhaceae*

Common Cat-tail	*Typha latifolia* L.
Narrow-leaved Cat-tail	*Typha angustifolia* L.

ARROW-GRASS FAMILY, *Juncaginaceae*

Arrow-grass	*Triglochin maritima* L.

GRASS FAMILY, *Gramineae*

Cheat	*Bromus secalinus* L.
Upright Chess	*Bromus racemosus* L.
Soft Chess	*Bromus mollis* L.
Downy Brome Grass	*Bromus tectorum* L.
Annual Bluegrass	*Poa annua* L.
Strong-Scented Love-Grass	*Eragrostis megastachya* (Koel.)
Small Tufted Love-Grass	*Eragrostis pilosa* (L.)
Tall Red-top	*Triodia flava* (L.)
Western Wheat-Grass	*Agropyron smithii* Rydb.
Quack-Grass	*Agropyron repens* (L.)
Poison Darnel	*Lolium temulentum* L.
Squirrel-Tail Grass	*Hordeum jubatum* L.
Little Barley	*Hordeum pusillum* Nutt.
Wild Barley	*Hordeum nodosum* L.
Velvet Grass	*Holcus lanatus* L.
Wild Oat	*Avena fatua* L.
Silver Hair-Grass	*Aira caryophyllea* L.
Common Wild Oat-Grass	*Danthonia spicata* (L.)
Poverty-Grass	*Sporobolus vaginiflorus* (Torr.)
Small Rush-Grass	*Sporobolus neglectus* Nash
Meadow-Foxtail	*Alopecurus pratensis* L.
Marsh-Foxtail	*Alopecurus geniculatus* L.
Nimble Will	*Muhlenbergia schreberi* J. F. Gmel.
Mexican Dropseed	*Muhlenbergia mexicana* (L.)
Wild Timothy	*Muhlenbergia racemosa* (Michx.)

Needle-and-thread-grass	*Stipa comata* Trin. & Rupr.
Porcupine-Grass	*Stipa spartea* Trin.
Seabeach-Needlegrass	*Aristida tuberculosa* Nutt.
Wire-Grass	*Aristida oligantha* Michx.
Poverty-Grass	*Aristida dichotoma* Michx.
Bermuda Grass	*Cynodon dactylon* (L.)
Crowfoot-Grass	*Dactyloctenium aegyptium* (L.)
Wiregrass	*Eleusine indica* (L.)
Holy Grass	*Hierochloe odorata* (L.)
Small Crab-Grass	*Digitaria ischaemum* (Schreb.)
Large Crab-Grass	*Digitaria sanguinalis* (L.)
Knotgrass	*Paspalum distichum* L.
Paspalum	*Paspalum ciliatifolium* Michx.
Sprouting Crab-Grass	*Panicum dichotomiflorum* Michx.
Old-witch Grass	*Panicum capillare* L.
Barnyard-Grass	*Echinochloa crusgalli* (L.)
Yellow Foxtail	*Setaria glauca* (L.)
Bristly Foxtail	*Setaria verticillata* (L.)
Green Foxtail	*Setaria viridis* (L.)
Fabers Foxtail	*Setaria faberii* Herrm.
Italian Millet	*Setaria italica* (L.)
Sandbur	*Cenchrus longispinus* (Hack.)
Sand-spur	*Cenchrus tribuloides* L.
Beard-grass	*Andropogon virginicus* L.
Johnson-Grass	*Sorgum halpense* (L.)

SEDGE FAMILY, Cyperaceae

Nut-grass	*Cyperus rotundus* L.
Yellow Nut-grass	*Cyperus esculentus* L.
Straw-colored Cyperus	*Cyperus strigosus* L.
Dark-green Bulrush	*Scirpus atrovirens* Willd.

SPIDERWORT FAMILY, Commelinaceae

Asiatic Dayflower	*Commelina communis* L.
Virginia Dayflower	*Commelina virginica* L.
Widow's Tears	*Tradescantia ohiensis* Raf.

PICKERELWEED FAMILY, Pontederiaceae

Water-hyacinth	*Eichornia crassipes* (Mart.)

RUSH FAMILY, Juncaceae

Path Rush	*Juncus tenuis* Willd.

LILY FAMILY, Liliaceae

Death Camass	*Z gadenus venenosus* **Rydb.**
Meadow Garlic	*Allium canadense* L.
Wild Garlic	*Allium vineale* **L.**
Star-of-Bethlehem	*Ornithogalum umbellatum* L.

201

DICOTYLEDONS

WAX-MYRTLE FAMILY, *Myricaceae*

Sweet-fern	*Comptonia peregrina asplenifolia* (L.)

HEMP FAMILY, *Cannabinaceae*

Hemp	*Cannabis sativa* L.

NETTLE FAMILY, *Urticaceae*

Slender Wild Nettle	*Urtica gracilis* Ait.
Stinging Nettle	*Urtica dioica* L.
Clearweed	*Pilea pumila* (L.)
False Nettle	*Boehmeria cylindrica* (L.)
Pellitory	*Parietaria pensylvanica* Muhl.

BUCKWHEAT FAMILY, *Polygonaceae*

Peach-leaved Dock	*Rumex altissimus* Wood
Curled Dock	*Rumex crispus* L.
Sheep Sorrel	*Rumex acetosella* L.
Green Sorrel	*Rumex acetosa* L.
Erect Knotweed	*Polygonum erectum* L.
Knot-grass	*Polygonum aviculare* L.
Marsh Smartweed	*Polygonum coccineum* Muhl.
Pinkweed	*Polygonum pensylvanicum* L.
Pale Smartweed	*Polygonum lapathifolium* L.
Princess-feather	*Polygonum orientale* L.
Common Smartweed	*Polygonum hydropiper* L.
Mild Water-pepper	*Polygonum hydropiperoides* Michx.
Wild Buckwheat	*Polygonum convolvulus* L.
Climbing False Buckwheat	*Polygonum scandens* L.

GOOSEFOOT FAMILY, *Chenopodiaceae*

Winged Pigweed	*Cycloloma atriplicifolium* (Spreng.)
Summer-cypress	*Kochia scoparia* (L.)
Nettle-leaved Goosefoot	*Chenopodium murale* L.
Upright Goosefoot	*Chenopodium urbicum* L.
Lamb's-quarters	*Chenopodium album* L.
Mexican-tea	*Chenopodium ambrosioides* L.
Halbred-leaved Orache	*Atriplex patula hastata* (L.)
Red Orache	*Atriplex rosea* L.
Russian Pigweed	*Axyris amaranthoides* L.
Russian Thistle	*Salsola kali tenuifolia* Tausch.

AMARANTH FAMILY, *Amaranthaceae*

Slender Pigweed	*Amaranthus hybridus* L.
Green Amaranth	*Amaranthus retroflexus* L.
Tumbleweed	*Amaranthus albus* L.
Prostrate Pigweed	*Amaranthus graecizans* L.
Spiny Amaranth	*Amaranthus spinosus* L.

FOUR-O'CLOCK FAMILY, *Nyctaginaceae*

Wild Four-o'clock	*Mirabilis nyctaginea* (Michx.)

POKEWEED FAMILY, *Phytolaccaceae*

Pokeweed	*Phytolacca americana* L.

CARPETWEED FAMILY, *Aizoaceae*

Carpetweed	*Mollugo verticillata* L.

PURSLANE FAMILY, *Portulacaceae*

Common Purslane	*Portulaca oleraceae* L.

PINK FAMILY, *Caryophyllaceae*

Corn Spurry	*Spergula arvensis* L.
Common Chickweed	*Stellaria media* (L.)
Larger Mouse-ear Chickweed	*Cerastium vulgatum* L.
Field-Chickweed	*Cerastium arvense* L.
Mouse-ear Chickweed	*Cerastium viscosum* L.
Corn Cockle	*Agrostemma githago* L.
White Campion	*Lychnis alba* Mill.
Bladder Campion	*Silene cucubalus* Wibel
Sleepy Catchfly	*Silene antirrhina* L.
Forking Catchfly	*Silene dichotoma* Ehrh.
Night-flowering Catchfly	*Silene noctiflora* L.
Bouncing-Bet	*Saponaria officinalis* L.

CROWFOOT FAMILY, *Ranunculaceae*

Small-flowered Crowfoot	*Ranunculus abortivus* L.
Meadow Buttercup	*Ranunculus acris* L.
Bulbous Buttercup	*Ranunculus bulbosus* L.
Low Larkspur	*Delphinium menziesii* DC.
European Barberry	*Berberis vulgaris* L.

POPPY FAMILY, *Papaveraceae*

Corn Poppy	*Papaver rhoeas* L.
Mexican Poppy	*Argemone mexicana* L.

CAPER FAMILY, *Capparidaceae*

Clammyweed	*Polanisia graveolens* Raf.
Pink Cleome	*Cleome serrulata* Pursh

MUSTARD FAMILY, *Cruciferae*

Vernal Whitlow-Grass	*Draba verna* L.
Hoary Alyssum	*Berteroa incana* (L.)
Field-Penny-Cress	*Thlaspi arvense* (L.)
Field Cress	*Lepidium campestre* (L.)
Wild Peppergrass	*Lepidium virginicum* L.
Shepherd's Purse	*Capsella bursa-pastoris* (L.)
Small-fruited False-flax	*Camelina microcarpa* Andrz.

Wild Radish	*Raphanus raphanistrum* L.
Garden Radish	*Raphanus sativus* L.
White Mustard	*Brassica hirta* Moench
Charlock	*Brassica kaber pinnatifida* (Stokes)
Indian Mustard	*Brassica juncea* (L.)
Black Mustard	*Brassica nigra* (L.)
Hare's-ear Mustard	*Coringia orientalis* (L.)
Hedge Mustard	*Sisymbrium officinale* (L.)
Tall Sisymbrium	*Sisymbrium altissima* L.
Marsh Water-cress	*Rorippa islandica* (Oeder)
Yellow Rocket	*Barbarea vulgaris* R.Br.

ORPINE FAMILY, *Crassulaceae*

Live-forever	*Sedum purpureum* (L.)

ROSE FAMILY, *Rosaceae*

Rough-fruited Cinquefoil	*Potentilla recta* L.
Rough Cinquefoil	*Potentilla norvegica* L.
Five-finger	*Potentilla canadensis* L.
White Avens	*Geum canadense* Jacq.
Yellow Avens	*Geum aleppicum strictum* (Ait.)
Tall Hairy Agrimonia	*Agrimonia gryposepala* Wallr.
Prairie Rose	*Rosa arkansana suffulta* (Greene)

PEA FAMILY, *Leguminosae*

Partridge-Pea	*Cassia fasciculata* Michx.
Sensitive Pea	*Cassia nictitans* L.
Large White Wild Indigo	*Baptisia leucantha* T. & G.
Large-bracted Wild Indigo	*Baptisia leucophaea* Nutt.
Rattle-box	*Crotalaria sagittalis* L.
Wild Lupine	*Lupinus perennis* L.
Hop-clover	*Trifolium agrarium* L.
Low Hop-clover	*Trifolium procumbens* L.
Yellow Sweet Clover	*Melilotus officinalis* (L.)
White Sweet Clover	*Melilotus alba* Desr.
Black Medic	*Medicago lupulina* L.
Stemless Loco	*Oxytropis lambertii* Pursh
Wild Licorice	*Glycyrrhiza lepidota* (Nutt.)
Showy Tick-trefoil	*Desmodium canadense* (L.)
Narrow-leaved Vetch	*Vicia angustifolia* Reichard
Wild Pea	*Lathyrus palustris* L.

WOOD-SORREL FAMILY, *Oxalidaceae*

Yellow Wood-sorrel	*Oxalis corniculata* L.
Upright Yellow Wood-sorrel	*Oxalis stricta* L.

GERANIUM FAMILY, *Geraniaceae*

Long-stalked Cranesbill	*Geranium columbinum* L.
Carolina Cranesbill	*Geranium carolinianum* L.
Small-flowered Cranesbill	*Geranium pusillum* L.
Storksbill	*Erodium cicutarium* (L.)

SPURGE FAMILY, *Euphorbiaceae*

Virginia 3-seeded Mercury	*Acalypha virginica* L.
Cypress Spurge	*Euphorbia cyparissias* L.
Snow-on-the-mountain	*Euphorbia marginata* Pursh
Flowering Spurge	*Euphorbia corollata* L.
Milk Purslane	*Euphorbia supina* Raf.
Large Spotted Spurge	*Euphorbia maculata* L.

CASHEW FAMILY, *Anacardiaceae*

Poison Ivy	*Rhus radicans* L.

MALLOW FAMILY, *Malvaceae*

Low Mallow	*Malva rotundifolia* L.
Musk Mallow	*Malva moschata* L.
Prickly Sida	*Sida spinosa* L.
Velvet Leaf	*Abutilon theophrasti* Medic.
Flower-of-an-hour	*Hibiscus trinonum* L.

ST. JOHN'S-WORT FAMILY, *Guttiferae*

Common St. John's-wort	*Hypericum perforatum* L.

PASSION-FLOWER FAMILY, *Passifloraceae*

Passion-flower	*Passiflora incarnata* L.

CACTUS FAMILY, *Cactaceae*

Western Prickly Pear	*Opuntia humifusa* Raf.

LOOSESTRIFE FAMILY, *Lythraceae*

Clammy Loosestrife	*Cuphea petiolata* (L.)

EVENING-PRIMROSE FAMILY, *Onagraceae*

Common Evening-primrose	*Oenothera biennis* L.
Biennial Gaura	*Gaura biennis* L.

PARSLEY FAMILY, *Umbelliferae*

Poison Hemlock	*Conium maculatum* L.
Water Hemlock	*Cicuta maculata* L.
Water Parsnip	*Sium suave* Walt.
Purple-stem Angelica	*Angelica atropurpurea* L.
Wild Parsnip	*Pastinaca sativa* L.
Wild Carrot	*Daucus carota* L.

PRIMROSE FAMILY, *Primulaceae*

Moneywort	*Lysimachia nummularia* L.
Scarlet Pimpernel	*Anagallis arvensis* L.

DOGBANE FAMILY, *Apocynaceae*

Periwinkle	*Vinca minor* L.
Large Periwinkle	*Vinca major* L.
Spreading Dogbane	*Apocynum androsaemifolium* L.
Indian Hemp	*Apocynum cannabinum* L.

MILKWEED FAMILY, *Asclepiadaceae*

Butterfly-weed	*Asclepias tuberosa* L.
Swamp-Milkweed	*Asclepias incarnata* L.
Common Milkweed	*Asclepias syriaca* L.
Whorled Milkweed	*Asclepias verticillata* L.
Florida Milkweed	*Asclepias longifolia* Michx.
Sandvine	*Ampelamus albidus* (Nutt.)
Black Swallow-wort	*Cynanchum nigrum* (L.)

CONVOLVULUS FAMILY, *Convolvulaceae*

Ivy-leaved Morning-glory	*Ipomea hederaceae* (L.)
Morning-glory	*Ipomea purpurea* (L.)
Wild Morning-glory	*Convolvulus sepium* L.
Bindweed	*Convolvulus arvensis* L.
Field Dodder	*Cuscuta pentagona* Engelm.
Large-seeded Alfalfa Dodder	*Cuscuta indecora* Choisy
Flax Dodder	*Cuscuta epilinum* Weihe
Clover Dodder	*Cuscuta epithymum* Murr.

WATERLEAF FAMILY, Hydrophyllaceae

Nyctelea	*Ellisia nyctelea* L.
Miami Mist	*Phacelia purshii* Buckl.

BORAGE FAMILY, *Boraginaceae*

Comfrey	*Symphytum officinale* L.
Blue Thistle	*Echium vulgare* L.
Corn Gromwell	*Lithospermum arvense* L.
Pearl Plant	*Lithospermum officinale* L.
Hound's-tongue	*Cynoglossum officinale* L.
Fiddle-neck	*Amsinckia barbata* Greene
Stickseed	*Lappula echinata* Gilib.

VERVAIN FAMILY, *Verbenaceae*

White Vervain	*Verbena urticifolia* L.
Blue Vervain	*Verbena hastata* L.
Hoary Vervain	*Verbena stricta* Vent.
Bracted Vervain	*Verbena bracteata* Lag. & Rodr.

MINT FAMILY, Labiate

Horehound	*Marribium vulgare* L.
Catnip	*Nepeta cataria* L.
Ground Ivy	*Glechoma hederaceae* L.
Heal-all	*Prunella vulgaris* L.
Motherwort	*Leonurus cardiaca* L.
Hemp Nettle	*Galeopsis tetrahit* L.
Henbit	*Lamium amplexicaule* L.
Wild Bergamot	*Monarda fistulosa* L.
Red Dead-Nettle	*Lamium purpureum* L.
Variegated Dead-Nettle	*Lamium maculatum* L.

American Pennyroyal	*Hedeoma pulegioides* (L.)
Spearmint	*Mentha spicata* L.
Peppermint	*Mentha piperita* L.
Creeping Whorled Mint	*Mentha gentilis* L.
Corn Mint	*Mentha arvensis* L.

NIGHTSHADE FAMILY, *Solanaceae*

Climbing Nightshade	*Solanum dulcamara* L.
Black Nightshade	*Solanum nigrum* L.
Horse Nettle	*Solanum carolinense* L.
Buffalo Bur	*Solanum rostratum* Dunal
Low Hairy Ground-Cherry	*Physalis pubescens* L.
Prairie Ground-Cherry	*Physalis lanceolata* Michx.
Clammy Ground-Cherry	*Physalis heterophylla* Noes
Apple-Of-Peru	*Nicandra physalodes* (L.)
Jimsonweed	*Datura stramonium* L.

FIGWORT FAMILY, *Scrophulariaceae*

Common Mullein	*Verbascum thapsus* L.
Moth Mullein	*Verbascum blattaria* L.
Kenilworth Ivy	*Cymbalaria muralis* Gaertn.
Butter-and-eggs	*Linaria vulgaris* Hill
Hare Figwort	*Scrophularia lanceolata* Pursh
Maryland Figwort	*Scrophularia marilandica* L.
Purslane Speedwell	*Veronica peregrina* L.
Corn Speedwell	*Veronica arvensis* L.

BROOM-RAPE FAMILY, *Orobanchaceae*

Broom-rape	*Orobanche ramosa* L.
Clover Broom-rape	*Orobanche minor* Sm.
Louisiana Broom-rape	*Orobanche ludoviciana* Nutt.

PLANTAIN FAMILY, *Plantaginaceae*

Common Plantain	*Plantago major* L.
Rugel's Plantain	*Plantago rugelii* Dene.
Buckhorn Plantain	*Plantago lanceolata* L.
Bracted Plantain	*Plantago aristata* Michx.
Pursh's Plantain	*Plantago purshii* R. & S.

MADDER FAMILY, *Rubiaceae*

Cleavers	*Galium aparine* L.
Rough Bedstraw	*Galium triflorum asprelliforme* Fern.
Rough Button-weed	*Diodia teres* Walt.

HONEYSUCKLE FAMILY, *Caprifoliaceae*

Japanese Honeysuckle	*Lonicera japonica* Thunb.
Buckbrush	*Symphoricarpos orbiculatus* Moench.

TEASEL FAMILY, *Dipsacaceae*

Teasel	*Dipsacus sylvestris* Huds.

GOURD FAMILY, Cucurbitaceae

Star Cucumber	*Sicyos angulatus* L.
Balsam Apple	*Echinocystis lobata* (Michx.)

BLUEBELL FAMILY, Campanulaceae

Venus's Looking-glass	*Specularia perfoliata* L.
Tall Bellflower	*Campanula americana* L.
Great Lobelia	*Lobelia siphilitica* L.
Indian-Tobacco	*Lobelia inflata* L.

COMPOSITE FAMILY, Compositae

Tall Ironweed	*Veronica altissima* Nutt.
Joe-Pye-weed	*Eupatorium dubium* Willd.
Boneset	*Eupatorium perfoliatum* L.
White Snakeroot	*Eupatorium rugosum* Houtt.
Broad-leaved Gum-plant	*Grindellia squarrosa* (Pursh.)
Tall Hairy Goldenrod	*Solidago rugosa* Ait.
Canada Goldenrod	*Solidago canadensis* L.
Stiff-leaved Goldenrod	*Solidago rigida* L.
Bushy Goldenrod	*Solidago graminifolia* (L.)
New England Aster	*Aster novae-angliae* L.
White Heath Aster	*Aster ericoides* L.
Calico Aster	*Aster lateriflorus* (L.)
Robin's-plantain	*Erigeron pulchellus* Michx.
Philadelphia Fleabane	*Erigeron philidelphicus* L.
Daisy-Fleabane	*Erigeron annuus* (L.)
White Top	*Erigeron strigosus* Muhl.
Horse-weed	*Erigeron canadensis* L.
Small Indian Tobacco	*Antennaria neglecta* Greene
Indian Tobacco	*Antennaria plantaginifolia* (L.)
Pearly Everlasting	*Anaphalis margaritacea* (L.)
Clammy Everlasting	*Gnaphalium macounii* Greene
Sweet Balsam	*Gnaphalium obtusifolium* L.
Low Cudweed	*Gnaphalium uliginosum* L.
Burweed Marsh Elder	*Iva xanthifolia* Nutt.
Great Ragweed	*Ambrosia trifida* L.
Hay-fever Weed	*Ambrosia artemisiifolia* L.
Western Ragweed	*Ambrosia psilostachya* DC.
Silver-leaf Poverty-weed	*Franseria discolor* Nutt.
Spiny Cocklebur	*Xanthium spinosum* L.
Cocklebur	*Xanthium orientale* L.
Common Sunflower	*Helianthus annuus* L.
Jerusalem Artichoke	*Helianthus tuberosus* L.
Saw-toothed Sunflower	*Helianthus grosseserratus* Martens
Giant Sunflower	*Helianthus giganteus* L.
Larger Bur-marigold	*Bidens laevis* (L.)
Nodding Bur-marigold	*Bidens cernua* L.
Beggar-ticks	*Bidens frondosa* L.
Tickseed-Sunflower	*Bidens coronata* (L.)

Western Tickseed-sunflower	*Bidens aristosa* (Michx.)
Spanish-needles	*Bidens bipinnata* L.
Galinsoga	*Galinsoga ciliata* (Raf.)
Small-flowered Galinsoga	*Galinsoga parviflora* Cav.
Fine-leaved Sneezeweed	*Helenium tenuifolium* Nutt.
Purple-headed Sneezeweed	*Helenium nudiflorum* Nutt.
Sneezeweed	*Helenium autumnale* L.
Fetid Marigold	*Dyssodia papposa* (Vent)
Yarrow	*Achillea millefolium* L.
Dog Fennel	*Anthemis cotula* L.
Corn Chamomile	*Anthemis arvensis* L.
Ox-eye Daisy	*Chrysanthemum leucanthemum* L.
Common Tansy	*Tanacetum vulgare* L.
Biennial Wormwood	*Artemesia biennis* Willd.
Annual Wormwood	*Artemesia annua* L.
Sagebrush	*Artemesia tridentata* Nutt.
Coltsfoot	*Tussilago farfara* L.
Fire-weed	*Erechtites hieracifolia* (L.)
Common Groundsel	*Senecio vulgaris* L.
Great Burdock	*Arctium lappa* L.
Smaller Burdock	*Arctium minus* (Hill)
Musk Thistle	*Carduus nutans* L.
Welted Thistle	*Carduus crispus* L.
Bull Thistle	*Circium vulgare* (Savi)
Tall Thistle	*Circium altissimum* (L.)
Canada Thistle	*Circium arvense* (L.)
Barnaby's Thistle	*Centaurea solstitialis* L.
Corn Flower	*Centaurea cyanus* L.
Russian Knapweed	*Centaurea repens* L.
Spotted Knapweed	*Centaurea maculosa* Lam.
Chicory	*Cichorium intybus* L.
Long-rooted Cat's-ear	*Hypochoeris radicata* L.
Fall Dandelion	*Leontodon autumnalis* L.
Ox-tongue	*Picris hieracioides* L.
Spiny Ox-tongue	*Picris echioides* L.
Vegetable Oyster	*Tragopogon porrifolius* L.
Yellow Goat's-beard	*Tragopogon pratensis* L.
Red-seeded Dandelion	*Taraxicum erythrospermum* Andrz.
Common Dandelion	*Taraxicum officinale* Weber
Field Sow-thistle	*Sonchus arvensis* L.
Common Sow-thistle	*Sonchus oleraceus* L.
Spiny-leaved Sow-thistle	*Sonchus asper* (L.)
Prickly Lettuce	*Lactuca scariola* L.
Wild Lettuce	*Lactuca canadensis* L.
Blue Lettuce	*Lactuca pulchella* (Pursh)
Rush Pink	*Lygodesmia juncea* (Pursh)
Orange Hawkweed	*Hieracium aurantiacum* L.
Yellow Paintbrush	*Hieracium pratense* Tausch

INDEX AND PICTURED-GLOSSARY

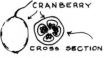

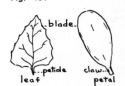

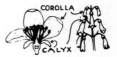
213

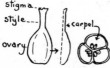

HOW TO KNOW THE WEEDS

CORDATE: heart-shaped. Fig. 436

Figure 436

Coringia 91
  orientalis 91
Corm 6
Corn-bind 54
Corn Campion 101
Corn Chamomile 185
Corn Cockle 101
Cornfield Horsetail 13
Corn Flower 175
Corn Gromwell 122
Corn-lily 132
Corn Mint 126
Corn Poppy 81
Corn-rose 81, 101
Corn Speedwell 143
Corn Spurry 96
Corn Thistle 176
COROLLA: the inner whorl of the perianth of a flower, composed of petals. 3 Fig. 437

Figure 437

COROLLA IRREGULAR: the petals of two or more shapes. Fig. 438

Figure 438

COROLLA REGULAR: the petals all alike. Fig. 439

Figure 439

CORONA: an appendage between the stamens and the corolla as in the milkweeds. Fig. 440

Figure 440

CORYMB: a flat-topped flower-cluster flowering from the outside to the inside. Fig. 441

Figure 441

Cotton
  Wild 115, 118
Cotton-weed 83, 118, 172
COTYLEDON: seed-leaf of the embryo containing stored food.
Couch-grass 37
Cowbane
  Spotted 107
Cow-bell 99
Cow Cress 89
Cow-grass 55
Cow-poison 67
Cow-quake 96
Cow Sorrel 59
Crabgrass 32
  Large 18
  Purple 18
  Small 18
  Sprouting 22
Crane's-bill
  Carolina 103
  Long-stalked 103
  Small-flowered 104
Crazy-weed 71
Creeper
  Poison 95
Creeping Charley 112, 127
Creeping Jenny 112, 132, 151
Creeping Loosestrife 112
Creeping Sow-thistle 160
Creeping Thistle 176
Creeping Whorled Mint 126
CRENATE: with rounded teeth. Fig. 442

Figure 442

CRENULATE: with very small rounded teeth.
Cress
  Bank 92

Bastard 88, 89
Bitter 92
Cow 89
Dock 155
Field 89
Marsh 90
Rocket 92
Water 94
Winter 92
CREST: an elevated appendage.
Crop-grass 32
Crotalaria 70
  sagittalis 70
Crowfoot 18, 32
  Kidney 68
  Small-flowered 65
  Tall 68
Crowfoot Family 66
Crowfoot-grass 32
Crow Garlic 43
Crown
  King's 75
Crown-of-the-field 101
Crown-weed 164
Crunchweed 94
Cuba-grass 20
Cuckolds 194
Cuckoo
  Snake 101
Cuckoo-button 174
Cucumber
  Bur 150
  One-seeded 150
  Star 150
  Wild 151
Cudweed
  Low 172
  Marsh 172
Cuphea 105
  petiolata 105
Cure-all
  King's 110
Curled Dock 59
Curled Thistle 178
Cursed Thistle 176
Cuscuta 133
  epilinum 134
  epithymum 133
  indecora 133
  pentagona 134
  plantiflora 133
Cycloloma 63
  atriplicifolium 63
Cymbalaria 141
  muralis 141
CYME: a broad, flattish inflorescence with its central or terminal flowers blooming first. Fig. 443

Figure 443

Cynanchum 115
  nigrum 115
Cynodon 17
  dactylon 17

215

Figure 444

Figure 445

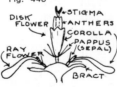

Figure 446

Figure 447

Figure 451

Figure 452

I

Figure 453

Figure 453½

Figure 454

J

K

Figure 455

Figure 456

Figure 457

Figure 458

Figure 459

O

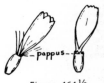

Figure 460

Figure 461

Figure 462

Figure 463

P

Figure 463½

Figure 464

Figure 464½

Figure 465

Figure 466

Figure 467

Figure 468

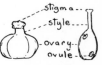

Figure 469

Figure 470

Figure 471

RECEPTACLE: the tip of the flower-stalk on which the floral parts are attached. Fig. 472

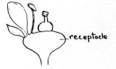

Figure 472

S

Figure 473

Figure 474

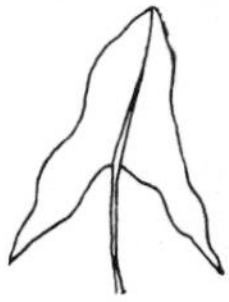

Figure 475

STIPULE: a leaf-like appendage at the base of the
leaf Fig. 479

Figure 479

STYLE: the part of the pistil that connects the ovary
and stigma. 4 Fig. 480

Figure 480

SUCCULENT: Juicy, fleshy.
SUPERIOR OVARY: one that
is above the calyx and
free from it. Fig. 481

Figure 481

T

TENDRIL: a twisting thread-
like part adapted for
clinging. Fig. 482

Figure 482

TERNATE: in threes. Fig.
483

Figure 483

Terry Cockle 99
Texas Thistle 136
Thimble-flower 128
Thistle
  Barnaby's 174
  Blue 119
  Buck 178
  Bull 177
  Bur 177
  Canada 176
  Corn 176
  Creeping 176
  Curled 178
  Cursed 176
  Green 176
  Horse 160
  Indian 149
  Milk 161
  Musk 178
  Nodding 178
  Plume 177
  Plumeless 178
  Queen Anne's 178
  Road-side 177
  Russian 62
  Small-flowered 176
  Spear 177
  Swine 160
  Tall 177
  Texas 136
  Tumbling 62
  Turkestan 176
  Welted 178
  Yellow 80
Thistle Mallow 83
Thlaspi 88
  arvense 88
Thorn Poppy 80
Thorny Amaranth 49
Thoroughwort
  Common 166
Thousand-leaf 184
Three-leaved Ivy 95
Three-seeded Mercury
  Virginia 49
Thunder-flower 81, 101
Thyme Dodder 133
Tickle-grass 19, 22
Tickseed-sunflower
  Western 197
Tick-trefoil
  Canada 73
  Showy 73
Tickweed 126
Timothy
  Water 24
  White 30
  Wild 28
Tipton-weed 81
Toad Pipes 13
Toad Sorrel 59

Toad-flax
  Yellow 141
Tobacco
  Indian 153, 171
  Ladies' 171, 172
  Rabbit 173
Tomato
  Strawberry 138
  Wild 137
Tongue
  Devil's 109
  Ox **157**
Tongue-grass 89
Toothwort 88
Torches 140
Tormentil 78
Tory-weed 120
Tradescantia 42
  chiensis 42
Tragopogon 156
  porrifolius 156
  pratensis 156
Trainasse 55
Tramp's Spurge 48
Treacle Mustard 91
Treaclewort 88
Tread-softly 137
Tree Clover 75
Tree-moss 47
Tree-primrose 110
Trefoil
  Hop 74
Trifolium 74
  agarium 74
  procumbens 74
Trigolochin 15
  maritima 15
Trinomial 1
Triodia 33
  flava 33
Triple-awned Grass
  Sea-beach 26
Triple-awn 26
Trumpet-weed 167
TUBE-FLOWER: a form of
  flower of the Compositae
  having a tubular corolla;
  also called disk-flower.
  Fig. 484

Figure 484

Tufted Spear-grass 33
Tumble-mustard 93
Tumble Panic-grass 22
Tumbleweed 22, 50, 63
  Russian 62
Tumbling Pigweed 50
Tumbling Thistle 62
Turkestan Thistle 176

Turkey-berry 148
Tussilago 189
  farfara 189
Twitch-grass 37
Two-penny Grass 112
Typha 14
  angustifolia 14
  latifolia 14

U

UMBEL: an inflorescence
with all the branches
arising at the same point.
Fig. 485

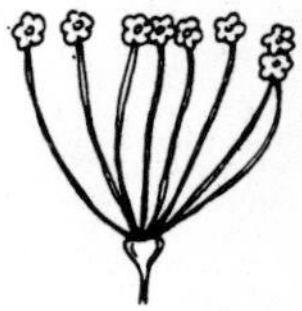

Figure 485

Umbrella-wort 61
Upland-fern 13
Upright Chess 36
Upright Goosefoot 65
Upright Spotted Spurge 46
Upright Yellow Wood-sorrel
  104
Urtica 51, 52
  dioica 52
  gracilis 51
UTRICLE: a small, bladdery,
one-seeded fruit.

V

Vanilla-grass 27
Variegated Spurge 48
Variety 1
Vegetable-oyster 156
Vegetative reproduction 6
Velvet-dock 140
Velvet Grass 30
Velvet Leaf 83
Venice's Mallow 82
Venus-cup 149
Venus's Looking-glass 151
Verbascum 140
  blattaria 140
  thapsus 140
Verbena 123, 124
  bracteata 123
  hastata 124
  stricta 123
  urticifolia 124
Verbena Family 123
Vernal Whitlow-grass 87
Veronia 173
  altissima 173
Veronica 142, 143
  arvensis 143
  peregrina 142

HOW TO KNOW THE WEEDS

Vervain
Blue 124
Bracted 123
False 124
Hoary 123
Mullein-leaved 123
Nettle-leaved 124
Prostrate 123
White 124
Woolly 123
Vetch
Colorado Loco 71
Common 72
Narrow-leaved 72
Smaller 72
Vetchling
Marsh 72
Viability 5
Vicia .72
angustifolia 72
VILLOUS: with long soft hairs.
Vinca 114
minor 114
Viper's Bugloss 119
Viper's-grass 119
Virginia Dayflower 41
Virginia Silk 118
Virginia Three-seeded Mercury 49
VISCID: sticky.
Volva 11

W

Wall-flower
Western 114
Wall Speedwell 143
Wampee 41
Wandering Jew 141
Wandering Milkweed 114
Warlock 95
Wartwort 172
Water-cress 94
Marsh 90
Yellow 90
Water Foxtail 24
Water-grass 21
Water-hemlock 107
Water Hyacinth 41
Water Mustard 92
Water-nerve-root 118
Water Parsnip 107
Water-pepper 57
Mild 58
Water Timothy 24
Water-torch 14
Wax-balls 49
Weather Glass
Poor-man's 113
Weather-grass 25
Welcome-to-our-house 47
Welted Thistle 178
Western Buckhorn 145
Western-flax 90
Western Prickly Pear 109
Western Quack-grass 38
Western Ragweed 165
Western Ripple-grass 145
Western Tickseed-sunflower 197
Western Wall-flower 114
Western Wheat-grass 38
Wheat
False 37
Wheat Oat 31

Wheat-grass 37
Western 38
Wheat-thief 36, 122
White Avens 77
White Balsam 173
White Ben 99
White Bird's-eye 97
White-blow 87
White Bottle 99
White Campion 101
White Charlock 91
White Cockle 101
White Evening-primrose 111
White-flowered Milkweed 48
White Goosefoot 64
White Horse 31
White Hoarhound 125
White Indian Hemp 118
White-margined Spurge 48
White Melilot 75
White-millet 75
White Mustard 93
White Pigweed 50
White Prickly Poppy 80
White Purslane 48
White Robin 101
White-root 117
White Sanicle 167
White Snakeroot 167
White Sweet-clover 75
White Timothy 30
White-top 188
Old 30
White Vervain 124
White-weed 164, 183, 188
Whitlow-grass
Vernal 87
WHORL: three or more parts arising at one node. Fig. 486

Figure 486

Whorled Chickweed 60
Whorled Milkweed 117
Wickens 37
Widow's Tears 42
Wild Asparagus 159
Wild Barley 19
Wild Bergamot 125
Wild Buckwheat 54
Wild Carrot 106
Wild-cat-grass 31
Wild Cotton 115, 118
Wild Cucumber 151
Wild Four-o'clock 61
Wild Garlic 42
Wild Hemp 129
Wild Hippo 48
Wild Hyssop 124
Wild Kale 91
Wild Lettuce 160
Wild Licorice 71

Wild Millet 23, 24
Wild Morning-glory 131
Wild Musk 102
Wild Mustard 94
Wild Nettle
Slender 51
Wild Oat 31
Wild-oat Grass
Common 31
Wild Onion 42, 43
Wild-pea 70, 72
Wild Parsnip 108
Wild Radish 91
Wild Rape 91
Wild Snapdragon 141
Wild Spinach 64
Wild Sunflower 190, 198, 199
Wild Sweet William 98
Wild-tansy 165
Wild Tare 72
Wild Timothy 28
Wild Tomato 137
Willow-herb 110
Willow-weed 56
Wind-witch 62
Winged Pigweed 63
Winter annual 6
Winter Cress 92
Winter Purslane 142
Winter-weed 97
Wire-grass 17, 25, 26, 27, 31, 32, 40
Witch-grass 37
Spreading 22
Witch's Money-bags 76
Witches'-pouches 88
Wode-whistle 108
Wood-cress
Yellow 90
Wood-grass 28
Wood-mat 120
Wood-sorrel
Procumbent 104
Upright Yellow 104
Yellow 104
Wood-sour 67
Woody Nightshade 136
Woolly Vervain 123
World's Wonder 98
Wormseed 64
Wormweed 85
Wormwood
Annual 170
Biennial 170
Roman 165
Wort
Umbrella 61
Wound Rocket 92

X

Xanthium 163
apinosum 163
orientale 163

Y

Yard-grass 32
Slender 40
Yarr 96
Yarrow 184
Yellow Avens 77
Yellow Daisy 184

229